MUSCULAR CHRISTIANITY

A CASE FOR SPIRITUAL AND PHYSICAL FITNESS

PAUL UPONI

"A crucial antidote to spiritual and physical weakness, and an explanation of their indissoluble relationship. If you don't read this, you're not going to make it – true!"

—**John Doyle,** host of Heck Off Commie!

"We live in a confusing time and a confusing world in which the lines between the sexes are being blurred as never before. That has resulted in the blurring of the definition of manhood as well. How refreshing to read the work of a young man who not only believes men and women are uniquely different, but that historic masculinity is to be desired in a man. Uponi has done a lot of research, from Plato to today, to put a unique perspective on manhood and physical fitness. I hope you enjoy it."

—**Dr. Paul Brushaber,** pastor and Doctor of Ministry

"As a Christian father that exercises and works as a personal trainer, I have always believed that Christians should be some of the fittest and healthiest people on the planet. God has given us a wonderful gift in the form of a physical body and blessed up with health, leaving us the responsibility to be stewards of our health and bodies. In the church body or church community, physical exercise is rarely talked about, and Paul raises a lot of points that are important to the Christian journey. *Muscular Christianity* captures some of the principles that are important to the Christian journey such as discipline and humility, which the Bible encourages us to practice. Paul highlights the importance of exercise and maintaining a strong body in addition to walking with God and this is something that every Christian should rave about!"

—**Nathaniel Agoye,** personal trainer and life coach

"Amidst the modern fitness culture that tends to glorify self and idolize our own appearances, Paul Uponi encourages us to dig deeper and explore what faith in fitness looks like. He presses into how we can prioritize the glorification of God, and the stewarding of one's body in biblical, theological, and practical ways."

—**Randall Royall,** natural pro bodybuilder

Acknowledgments

I would like to first give special thanks to my loving family. Thanks to my mother (Uzoma Uponi) and father (Matthew Uponi) for persisting and dealing with all the work that was required to raise a kid like me. They have been very influential in my faith and fitness journey. For one thing, they paid an exorbitant amount of money for me to attempt to play sports at a high level. Hopefully, they don't think it was all a waste. Also, they sacrificed a lot for my academic development. I would not have been able to write this book if it weren't for their loving sacrifices. My mother, who is a creative writer and editor, also helped edit this book. She has written three books of her own, *ColourBLIND*, *Whispers from Yesteryears*, and *ColorSTRUCK*, so I know I am in good hands.

Thanks to my brother Michael for being the younger brother with whom I can always be honest. Thanks to my second-oldest brother, Matthew-Daniel (MD), for providing subtle support in my fitness and life journey. Thanks to my oldest brother, David, for being more hands-on in my pursuit of entrepreneurial endeavors. And thanks to my cousin, Joshua, for being like a brother on whom I can always depend.

I would also like to thank all the subscribers of my YouTube channels DrUpauli and Upauli Athletics for supporting me all these years. A big shout-out to my friends Steven, Katie, Luke, the boys at the Chad Factory, and others who wish to remain anonymous. If it weren't for you all, the ideas in this book would have remained stuck in my head and never articulated in a book. I would never have put pen to paper if it weren't for your push and encouragement.

Finally, and most importantly, I thank our Lord above. He gave someone as undeserving as me the chance to give glory to Him in a feeble way through this book. Everything I have done to make this book a reality has been done to bring glory to Him.

Contents

Preface

————————×( )×————————

According to Wikipedia, "Muscular Christianity is a philosophical movement that originated in England in the mid-nineteenth century, characterized by a belief in patriotic duty, discipline, self-sacrifice, masculinity, and the moral and physical beauty of athleticism."[1]

I didn't even realize Muscular Christianity was a thing until I read that. In hindsight, the idea was something I had thought about but had never been able to coherently articulate or put a label on. When I learned that it exists, I became thoroughly intrigued and began to research it. Some friends who subscribe to my YouTube channel "DrUpauli"[2] had for months been telling me to write a book, and I figured this would be the perfect topic.

I can relate to this topic because this was how I forayed into spirituality. Growing up, I was heavily involved in physical exercise. At the same time, I lived in a Christian home. This is why I have chosen to write a book on their intersection, focusing on this small aspect of Christianity.

The phrase Muscular Christianity originated from Charles Kingsley's book *Two Years Ago*, published in 1857. Kingsley listed the core ideas of the philosophy as follows: "Physical strength, religious certainty, and the ability to shape and control the world around one."[3] The former American President Theodore Roosevelt was raised in a household that practiced Muscular Christianity and was a prominent adherent to the movement. Roosevelt promoted physical strength and health as well as an active pursuit of Christian ideals in personal life and politics. The Young Men's Christian Association's (YMCA) focus on fellowship and athletics is another practical application of Muscular Christianity.[4]

1

Although various websites and books mention Muscular Christianity, I have not yet seen a thorough articulation of this philosophy and its implications. Hopefully, I can do justice to that in this book. And hopefully, this book meaningfully adds to the body of knowledge on the subject.

Introduction

—————————————×( )×—————————————

In our era we have seen increased interest in the combination of spiritual and physical fitness. Wellness and self-improvement initiatives have become very popular. We are a generation that obsessively practices daily healthy habits with the promise of future physical and mental health rewards. These have been made necessary to deal with our collective state of anxiety, confusion, and apathy that have resulted from the world of social media and other modern pressures. If you search enough, you will find exercise posited as a potential solution to these issues because it addresses nearly all of them and more. In my opinion, exercise is the single most effective self-help tool. But self-help by itself can only do so much. It tends to work more like a painkiller—providing only temporary relief, not substantive healing. Self-help strategies are unable to dig deeper than surface issues; they fail to address the deeper philosophical and spiritual issues.

As the religious population continues to decline, contemporary women may look to astrology for spirituality. Men, on the other hand, search for something to satisfy the desire for a substantive, difficult, and regimented way of living. This is why they are looking to ancient Stoic philosophers like Marcus Aurelius, Seneca, and Epictetus, along with contemporary wisdom from self-improvement figures like Jordan Peterson, Andrew Tate, Ryan Holiday, Jocko Willink, and David Goggins. Most of the contemporary self-improvement figures are successful authors and podcasters with millions of book sales and podcasts with millions of listeners. Most of them being male. Whether they know it or not, these influential figures are filling a spiritual lacuna in the hearts of men. As their philosophies penetrate the mind and body, they will inevitably impact the souls of their adherents due to the

3

interconnectedness of the human self.

These philosophers tell their adherents that a good life is a virtuous life and that a virtuous life is a difficult life. They call their adherents to move away from a life of hedonism and nihilism to embrace a life of suffering and responsibility. They call men to a life of spiritual honesty and moral challenge. This especially impacts the souls of men. But these philosophies similarly leave a lot to be desired. This is why I believe people ought to consider Christianity and mix it with exercise. In this book, I will delve into the interconnection between faith and self-improvement, with an emphasis on physical exercise.

It seems clear to me that the physical, mental, and spiritual efforts we cram into our modern lives are not enough to bring us wholeness by themselves. It is my hope that some people who are struggling with how they can experience a balanced, wholesome life that properly combines their physical, mental, and spiritual entities, will find encouragement and practical help from this book.

The present cultural crises in the Western world has reignited the yearning and the calls for a return to traditional values to restore some sanity to society. This book offers the God-fearing Christian man as the solution to the crises. I opine that Muscular Christianity is one thing that the world is searching for. It is my hope that through *Muscular Christianity: A Case for Spiritual and Physical Fitness*, I can help shift the masculine spirituality tide away from hollow secular sources and into the ultimate source of Christianity.

But I must give a word of caution to my readers: For some, the ideas articulated in this book will challenge your presuppositions about Christianity; for others, this book will invigorate your faith. There may, however, be some who get upset with some of the content of this book. That is usually the case with matters of religion, especially with some of the topics I cover in this book. I encourage you to read to the end; hopefully, you will increase your understanding of some of our Christian beliefs.

This book will explain why Christians should care about physical fitness, why men are leaving the church in droves, what can be done about it, and how sports and fitness link to the mind and soul—which help cultivate virtues that make you a better Christian. Most of the material in this book comes from my independent readings on adjacent subjects, my undergraduate psychology studies, my personal experiences, my observations, and my insights.

I will start with a general discussion about the body, mind, and soul, explain their practical applications, and then provide an analysis of different types of exercises in a brief, practical guide that will help to direct you toward living a Muscular Christian life.

Part I:
Understanding Your Body

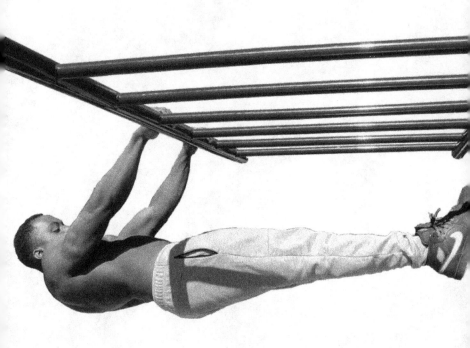

CHAPTER 1
Your Body Is a Temple

―✕ ✕―

You created my inmost being; you knit me together in my mother's
womb. I praise you because I am fearfully and wonderfully made;
your works are wonderful, I know that full well.
–Psalm 139:13–14

What a piece of work is man! How noble in reason!
How infinite in faculties! In form and moving,
how express and admirable! In action how like an angel!
–William Shakespeare

Christianity teaches that the human body is a temple for glorifying God and should be treated as such. A temple is a holy place in which God's Spirit dwells. Thus it ought to be kept clean and in good condition. God took His time in knitting each person from the moment they were conceived in their mother's womb. He carefully and wonderfully made mankind in His distinct image. This puts an obligation on every person to treat their body with respect.

There is a concept known as "mind-body dualism." It is the erroneous idea that the mind and body are two completely distinct entities. This idea leads people to ignore their bodies. A related concept is Gnosticism, which also applies substance dualism but to an even greater extreme. Not only does it see the mind, soul, and body as separate, it also sees them as antagonistic forces. Gnosticism regards the human body as a fleshy prison that can be manipulated or discarded in favor of the mental or spiritual facets it houses.

Some Christians similarly elevate the spiritual over the physical and believe that what is inside counts more than what is outside. They prioritize the spiritual realm over the physical and perceive internal qualities as more significant than external ones. They use this as an excuse to disregard their bodies and treat it carelessly. They think they should pay attention only to their spiritual growth and not care about their physical bodies. In some sense they are correct. The mind, body, and spirit are connected, but they are not the same thing, nor do they carry the same importance. If a decision has to be made, the spirit must always take priority, with the mind and the body aiding it. But that line of thinking, if taken by itself, misses the bigger picture, which is that the mind, body, and spirit work together to aid the life of the soul. This is similar to how the sun and moon work together to sustain life on earth. The sun and moon aid in maintaining life on earth and would become meaningless physical components without their relation to the earth. So too do the mind and body aid the spirit and become meaningless properties without their relationship to the spirit.

What God Gave You

Your mind was given to you. It is a rational manifestation of your soul. It gives you the ability to articulate what you profoundly intuit within your spirit. It also gives you the ability to understand and communicate the things you learn.

Your body was given to you. It is the physical manifestation of your soul. It houses your spirit and is the vehicle through which you experience this life. It's a marvelous blessing from God and should be treated with respect. You have only one body, so you should take the utmost care of it and use it optimally.

The Bible says that in the beginning God created Adam and Eve in His likeness to have dominion over the earth. He also instructed them to use their bodies to create more bodies ("Be fruitful and multiply!").

This means we are all like Adam who was particularly distinguished among creation.

Thus your body is not your own. It is on loan from your Maker. Why wouldn't you want to keep it sharp? You cannot make one hair white or black. Even the hair colors offered at the hair salons and barber shops fade with new growth. You cannot breathe oxygen into your lungs and give yourself life. The Lord is the one who breathes into humanity the breath of life and graciously sustains that life. The least you can do in response to this gift from God is to take care of your body. Think of self-care as a demonstration of your gratitude.

God gave you an incredible, intricately woven body that is infinitely complex. A single gram of DNA holds 215 petabytes of information. That's 215 million gigabytes. That can fit the entire King James Bible in plain text 54 million times. Due to what is called gene expression, each cell knows exactly what it needs to do in accordance with where it is in the body. This is what makes sure that the elbow acts like an elbow, the knee acts like a knee, the eye acts like an eye, and internal organs act as they are supposed to. Scientific research has shown that although humans commonly share 99.9 percent similarity in DNA, the 0.1 percent where we differ is responsible for the wide variation we see across the human species. Despite this, no two human beings are alike, and nearly every human being is easily identifiable.[1] The smallest human blood vessels (capillaries) are 5 micrometers thick.[2] To give some perspective, the smallest strands of hair measure 17 micrometers thick[3]—more than three times thicker than blood vessels. These are the vessels that play the vital role of transporting blood and oxygen throughout the entire human body. They are so tightly packed that if we were to take all the blood vessels out of an average child and lay them out in a single line, the line would stretch over 60,000 miles (96,560.64 kilometers). For an adult, it would be close to 100,000 miles

(160,934.4 kilometers) long. That length would wrap around the Earth's circumference four times over.[4]

Our brain has 100 billion brain cells, called "neurons," and 125 trillion synapses (the junction between the neurons) in the cerebral cortex alone. That's more than 1,500 times the number of stars in the Milky Way galaxy. Those neurons all communicate with each other at speeds that can reach up to 200 mph (322 kph)[5] while perfectly coordinating to send neurons to your arm, allowing you to utilize your bicep, shoulder, and finger muscles with precise coordination in order to lift this book up with the precise amount of strength.[6] If you are reading this, your eyes are also working in order to see all of this, and your verbal comprehension is working in order to read and make sense of the material. All of this is controlled by your neurons and synapses. We are all deliberately and delicately made, meticulously complex, and infinitely unique in our construction.

In addition to our body's delicate design, we are extremely adaptable. Blind people have heightened hearing and spatial awareness to make up for their lack of sight.[7] They can use the tactile information they get from the ground beneath their feet, from their cane, or from their hands to create a mental layout of an entire room. This creates an ersatz vision.

Studies have also shown that the brain can be rewired and reconditioned to think in different ways. For example, the brains of people who meditate and pray often seem to, over time, develop in a different way from the brains of people who do not pray as often. Their brains show stronger connections in both the ventromedial prefrontal cortex[8] and the anterior insular cortex.[9] These are the parts of your brain that are responsible for emotional regulation, empathy, and the ability to cope with stressful situations. Dr. Andrew Newberg, author of *How God Changes Your Brain: Breakthrough Findings from a Leading*

Neuroscientist, calls the anterior cingulate the "neurological heart." It sits just behind the frontal lobe. This is also considered to be the part of the brain that most clearly distinguishes humans from animals.[10] It is responsible for all our higher-order functions such as decision-making, impulse control, emotion, ethics, and morality. Prayer increases activity in this area.[11] Unlike animals, we are made in God's image. The spirit and the mind are connected. We are made for a purpose. We are made for prayer. More broadly, we are made to bring glory to God.

Some people may object to this and claim that these benefits are derived from merely being "spiritual but not religious," and they try to prove their point by pointing out that eastern variations of meditations boast similar results. The problem I have with this is that prayer is not only something in which you contemplate the abstract outside world, it is also a personal conversation. This has been shown to have unique benefits. Secular psychologist Barbara Fredrickson states, "Imagining yourself having a conversation with exemplary people is as good as talking to them. . . . [It] leaves you with an inner voice that guides you through challenging times."[12] That sounds a lot like prayer and the Holy Spirit providing us with the perfect example of virtue. Other meditation methods do not account for this conversational or relational element. There is also the fact that God's nature has different facets. Sometimes we view Him as a benevolent, loving, and forgiving God. But sometimes we envision Him as a central authority who punishes evil. In the former, we find the benefits discussed above, and in the latter, we will likely activate our primitive limbic system, which activates fear and anger. The ability to have both circuits maximally functioning is another thing that separates Christian prayer from secular meditation. Sometimes God feels more personal, sometimes He is seen as someone who is higher above. A lot of this is discussed in chapter 6 of *How God Changes the Brain*. The Christian Philosopher Michael

Jones, creator of the "InspiringPhilosophy" YouTube channel, covers this in his video "Is Christianity Harmful?"[13]

A study done on London taxi drivers showed a measurable brain difference in their hippocampus. This is the part of the brain that is associated with spatial cognition and memory and helps them navigate the dynamic world of driving.[14] All the neurons in the human body are incredibly intricate and complex, yet all are able to quickly and seamlessly work together in harmony to adapt to situations.

The complex ways our bodies have been made can only be described as masterful gifts from God. The way the body works as a full circuit is something that is truly amazing. The time and effort that must have been put into creating the masterpiece that is the human body can only mean that our Maker created our bodies with great care and love. We cannot treat this gift with careless abandon.

He gave each body an accompanying spirit. I said earlier that we should put more emphasis on the spirit and the soul over the physical body, but oftentimes the Bible treats all as one unit, one person, one human being. The Bible teaches that we consist of body, soul, and spirit. We are not a body that happens to have a spirit, or a spirit that happens to have a body; we are souls, and we are bodies. In 1 Thessalonians 5:23 we read a prayer by Paul: "May your whole spirit, soul and body be preserved blameless at the coming of our Lord Jesus." Our material bodies are what we see; the soul and spirits are the parts of us we cannot see. Both are spoken of in the same context. Just as the physical body works together to keep a person alive, it also works to host the soul and the spirit. This tripartite relationship is not only discussed in the Bible, it is also affirmed in science and in metaphysics.

Body, Mind, and Spirit

If you have your shoulders forward, rounded, chest tucked in and head down, not only will you look small and defeated, but you will feel small and defeated. But if you stand up with your shoulders back, chest out, and head held high, you will both present and feel as if you are strong and victorious.[15] There is a clear correlation between physical posture/well-being and mental posture/well-being. We are body, mind, and soul composites, and the material world is but a physical expression of the spiritual world. To better understand this, we need to look into the evolutionary and biological premises behind physical exercise because it can shed light on the way God made us.

I once shared a meme online with a rather misleading headline. It read, "Humans are not evolved to exercise, says Harvard prof."[16] I found it hilarious because I presumed it was one more "expert" saying something completely ridiculous to provide a "scientific" excuse for lazy people to rationalize their life decisions, providing them an "intellectual" outlet to wallow in sloth and mask it as a virtue. But after persisting and reading through the entire article, I discovered that I had been wrong in my presumption. The article headline had distilled nuanced evolutionary biology to something only vaguely resembling the actual point in order to get more clicks. And it worked—I fell for it. The professor's argument in the article was that from an evolutionary perspective, senselessly exerting energy is not good for people to do. Instead of sweating for the heck of it, our bodies want us to save our energy for running from the forces of nature. I don't completely agree with this take, (dancing and playing games probably play some part in our design) but it does shed light on the biological and evolutionary reasons we exercise.

Reinterpretation of the Meme in Reference.

Before the age of industrialization, our species was constantly on the move. We didn't have water with the flip of a switch, we had to go to a well, lake, or river to fetch it. If we wanted food, we had to grab it from a tree or kill an animal. As humans, we are meant to move. It's only recently in the modern era that we can, and are almost encouraged, to live a sedentary life.

Exercise is important for our brains. This is because it puts our brains in a "shocked" state. Back in the old days, if you were sprinting, that meant you were in danger. Maybe you were running away from a bear and your brain had to work a mile a minute. If you were swimming, perhaps you were hunting a fish or were being chased by a big fish, so your brain was sparked to start thinking more—to remember the location, to create mental landmarks of where you were when

16

things happened. In modern society, we don't face those problems. All that we need is usually at our fingertips; we don't have to move. When we are sedentary, we're telling our brains we are safe and that it doesn't need to work. While this is largely true, it is surely a sub-optimal use of our brains.

We exercise to navigate and prepare for the environment. Our environment now is not very physically demanding compared to what our ancestors faced, and our bodies have adapted to this lifestyle. So our brains aren't shocked as much. However, a few hundred years of technological advancement cannot change how we were designed. We are a moving species, designed to keep moving. We need to do so in order to reach our maximum human potential. We are not designed to waste energy, so at face value exercise doesn't seem to make any sense because our bodies will voluntarily use up energy. Now we must consciously and voluntarily exercise since movement is no longer a natural and essential part of our routine. A regular exercise regime can help you stay in tune with this facet of your natural neural makeup.

The Bible doesn't comment a lot on the need for exercise because the lifestyle of earlier generations naturally required long hours of physical work. Physicality was by and large assumed. Remember that the Bible is a spiritual book and focuses on spiritual issues. The occasional acknowledgment of exercise it contains is mostly to help illustrate points, as in 1 Corinthians 9:27 and Hebrews 12:1.

Spiritual fitness is, of course, more important than physical fitness in the absolute sense for the simple reason that eternal life with God is more desired than this earthly existence, which eventually comes to an end. Nevertheless, physical fitness can enhance Christian living, which can help make the quest for eternity more fulfilling. Our body literally houses our soul. Our soul will join our Creator when we die. Should we not care deeply about the vessel that houses our soul? Our bodies should be in their best shape to help our souls be in their best shape. G. E. L. Cotton says, "God was the creator of our bodies, as well as our minds. His workmanship included physical as well as mental powers and faculties. In developing both we are serving Him who made us, no less than when we kneel in prayer."[17]

Remember that you cannot do most things our bodies were designed for if you do not take care of your body. Things like playing with your kids and living an active and full life might become burdensome chores for you. Even serving God will become more difficult without a maximally functional body. How long can you serve your church with a spoiled spine? How long can you feed the needy with a nonfunctional knee? Your body is meant to be enjoyed by you and by others and to be applied in service to others and to your God. It is a gift. How long can you enjoy this gift if you do not take care of it? If I bought you a beautiful present, I would want you to take care of it, enjoy it, and make the most of it. God wants us to enjoy living in the body He has given us, and we should be good stewards by preserving it until its natural end when our spirits reconnect with Him in heaven and our bodies are made new.

Mind and Body

Our mind and body aren't disconnected from one another. From ancient philosophy to modern medicine, the close and meaningful connection between the mind and body has been clear. The Japanese called this *kokoro* (with the kanji 心). The ancient Greeks had the word *kalokagathia* which refers to the harmonious combination of bodily, moral, and spiritual beauty and virtue. They also had the concepts of physiognomy and phrenology. The soft scientific concepts state that one's cranial (phrenology) and facial (physiognomy) structures could be used to ascertain one's character. Scholarly theologians and philosophers may use the word hylomorphism. Hylomorphism is a concept used by the likes of Aristotle and Thomas Aquinas to explain how objects consist of material (matter) and immaterial (form) components. These components ultimately come together to form what we recognize as meaningful objects. Neither matter nor form possess any significance individually; they take on meaning only once they are observed in unison.

The writers of the Bible also knew this. This is why the law used to require men to be circumcised to be part of God's covenant. It is why we wash people in water when we baptize them. In a sense we are physically and spiritually cleaning them. It is why traditional Catholics make a sign of the cross when praying. They are performing a physical ritual that expresses a deeper spiritual connection.

Physical health and mental health are branches from the same root. It makes sense that they work in harmony. 1 Corinthians 6:19–20 says, "Do you not know that your bodies are temples of the Holy Spirit, who is in you, whom you have received from God? You are not your own; you were bought at a price. Therefore honor God with your bodies." Third John 1:2 also demonstrates the link between physical and spiritual health. It says, "Dear friend, I pray that you may enjoy good health and that all may go well with you, even as your soul is getting along well."

Medical research has confirmed that when you face prolonged, chronic mental stress, your blood pressure goes up. This is called a psychosomatic response. Conversely, when you exercise, you release dopamine, which brings the blood pressure under control. So it is not only physical health that influences your lifespan but also mental health. Everything is connected. Physical health is connected to the soul and can bring healing to the mind.

There's a fascinating concept called the "mind-muscle

connection." It's the idea that during resistance training, when you think about the muscle you're working—really focusing on the fibers running through that muscle group during an exercise—you will increase activation in that area. Several studies have shown this to be a valid concept producing tangible results.[18] When you *think* about training a muscle, it actually works that muscle more. Studies have even shown that simply thinking about exercising can help you grow muscle, even when you aren't physically exercising.[19] The same is seen with basketball players and free throw shooting. When people visualize themselves shooting and making free throws in basketball, it has been shown in some instances to be just as effective as physically practicing it.[20] This shows that the mind affects the body.

Vanity VS Appreciation

In the quest to become fit and maintain physical fitness, it is also important to keep modesty front and center. Physical health is correlated with physical attraction, so it is likely you will become more attractive when your body is toned from exercising. This is one of the rewards for your hard work. While this is good news, we should be careful not to allow this to devolve into vanity and promote jealousy or lust. This point is similar to choosing to dress well. There is a fine line between vanity and appreciation; and although there's nothing wrong with dressing nicely to look good or impress others, there are certain boundaries that you should not cross. Whether you are exercising and keeping fit, or dressing well, it needs to be done modestly and in the right spirit. Conduct yourself in such a way as to not intentionally tempt another person to stumble. First Corinthians 10:31–32 instructs us that "whether you eat or drink or whatever you do, do it all for the glory of God. Do not cause anyone to stumble, whether Jews, Greeks, or the church of God."

CHAPTER 2
Athletic Christianity

›—‹ ›–‹

Take care of your body as if you were going to live forever;
and take care of your soul as if you were going to die tomorrow.
–St. Augustine

For the Spirit God gave us does not make us timid,
but gives us power, love and self-discipline.
–2 Timothy 1:7

When people talk about exercise, they often focus on the plethora of benefits it can give you: It's *good for your heart,* gives you *big muscles,* and helps you *lose weight.* While these are good benefits in their own rights, they may not be compelling enough for everyone.

Good for your heart is hard to conceptualize for most people and appeals mostly to older folk. *Losing weight* is a huge problem that almost all first-world countries are facing, but it certainly doesn't apply to everyone; so this reason may be superficially meaningless to the thinner members of the population. In addition, data shows that exercise isn't even the most effective way to lose weight. Giving you *big muscles* or improving your physique is something everyone can relate to, and it's probably something we've all desired at some point. But for many people, even that isn't reason enough to get into an exercise regime.

Historically, Christians did not always take issues of physical fitness seriously, especially in the sports realm. The early church, or at least some of their teachers, rejected gladiator battles as savage and only meant for brutish entertainment. Gladiator battles were considered pagan rituals.[1] And, truth be told, gladiator sports, the most popular sports at the time, were bloody as the gladiators would sometimes fight to the death, killing each other for nothing substantive. Just for sport.

In later centuries, both Catholics and Protestants began to recognize other sports, although they still regarded them as a waste of time. In the nineteenth century, the conservative American South viewed football as the revival of pagan ideals of masculinity, not Christian masculinity. Southern Christians denounced sports as "animal, barbarous, brutal, savage and carnal."[2] These attributes were in stark contrast to the educational environment they sought for their kids. Their ideal college environment was a "pious, highly disciplined collegiate environment that left no room for the passion or frivolity that surrounded intercollegiate football."[3] They regarded sports as a heathen event, a waste of precious time. A Baptist editor in the 1880s commented that baseball was a "murderous game," more brutal than a bullfight, more reprehensible than a prize fight, and more deadly than modern warfare.[4] To be fair, the horrors of the world wars had not yet begun at this time, so he may not have made this comparison if he had experienced what we consider modern warfare. Still, this was a very passionate critique and an over-corrective response to the ghoulish gladiator battles.

On some level I can sympathize with this view. I can see why, on the surface, these sports were (and in some circles still are) viewed as being contrary to core Christian values. But having played sports competitively in my formative years, I know that they are more calculated than mindless aggression. My involvement in sports has provided me with opportunities to learn and articulate many Christian values and lifestyle choices—values like humility, temperance, and respect. Here are some things I have learned:

1. Humility

I like to think there are two kinds of humility. The first is what I will call moral humility; the second is what I will call personal humility. Moral humility is what I believe the Bible wants everyone to practice. It is the opposite of pride, which is basically thinking that you are somehow superior to other people and therefore deserve favors. Moral pride is considered the worst of the seven deadly sins (pride, envy, gluttony, lust, wrath, greed, and sloth) and hinders spiritual progress. Moral pride is referred to as the gateway to all the other deadly sins.

The only way to overcome pride is to change your thought patterns, to recognize that along with all of humanity you share the potential for evil—and that despite your attributes, you are not intrinsically superior to, or more deserving than, any other person. In the Christian tradition, we see that Lucifer was proud and tried to rise above God to usurp His place in heaven. That is why he was banished from heaven. Pride was what also made Adam and Eve eat the forbidden fruit because they wanted to be like God. In other words, moral pride is what makes a person think they are like God or don't need God.

Moral humility is the opposite of moral pride and was at the core of Jesus' life. It was His humility that made Him come down to earth to show us how to live. When He was on earth, Jesus was infinitely better than any of us, but He acted as though He were one of us. This is the ultimate example of moral humility. A noteworthy quote in the Scriptures says, "Have the same mindset as Christ Jesus: who, being in very nature God, did not consider equality with God something to be used to his own advantage; rather, he made himself nothing by taking the very nature of a servant, being made in human likeness. And being found in appearance as a man, he humbled himself by becoming obedient to death—even death on a cross!" (Philippians 2:5–8). If athletes refrain from harboring hatred for, and a sense of superiority over, their opponents—while maintaining self-confidence—they can be free from moral pride.

Then there is personal pride. This is the idea that you believe you are better than people at particular things, like Ronaldo claiming he is the greatest soccer player. This is the type of pride people usually think of, which makes them think that pride isn't necessarily a bad thing. I use the word "pride" here because this is how we have colloquially used the word, but this is arguably not far from humility. Humble comes from the Latin word *humus*, which could be translated as "grounded." This means that you are being realistic. If this is the case, one could argue that acknowledging the fact that you are better than others at certain things is actually a realistic opinion. Similarly, Paul says in Romans 12:3 that we should think of ourselves not inordinately high but to think of ourselves with "sober judgement." Acknowledge your success, but don't boast about it, and certainly don't identify yourself with it. That is how personal pride can slip into moral pride.

I believe sports can instill both moral and personal humility. When you lose, you are often physically overwhelmed. This will quickly and effectively bring you back down from whatever pompous pedestal you may have placed yourself on. A story I often tell from personal experience during my high school days is how I boasted all year long about how physically strong and fast I naturally was and how I had never been injured in my years playing basketball. But one day during P.E. class, my classmates and I had to race each other to see who could run back and forth down the court the fastest. I had a reputation for being the fastest in my grade, so I had to win this. When the race started, I was in the lead. But some classmates started to catch up. I couldn't allow myself to be seen as anything less than the unparalleled fastest, so I began to run so hard that I started leaning forward. This caused me to start stumbling. On the last leg of the race, I lost my footing, fell, and smashed my wrist and head against the concrete wall. This made me lose consciousness for many seconds. In fact, I don't remember any of this happening. I probably experienced some kind of retrograde amnesia after the fact, but I was told that this is what happened when I woke up. Immediately after, I was rushed to the hospital emergency room. It turned out I had a mild concussion, a broken left wrist, and a bruised right wrist. And, oh yeah, basketball tryouts were the next day.

Thank God I only suffered broken and bruised body parts. My classmates told me it looked much worse. Some were even afraid I had died. It was a profound lesson on the frailty of human life and the humiliation that often results from obsessive personal pride. After the shock of the event had worn off, I became the butt of all jokes. And I deserved it. I was humorously known as the guy who broke his wrist running into a wall. Every time someone asked me how I broke my wrist, I had to tell them the truth. That truth being that I had comically run into a wall. It made me sound like a foolish brute. And I was. This experience was very effective in getting me off my high horse, thinking I was better than I actually was—a big lesson in the need for personal humility. Lucky for me, I was still allowed on the basketball team via the good word of my teammates (and the team had a very successful season that year, winning the championship and going undefeated in all the games we played after I recovered).

We are allowed to be *proud* of something but not be *prideful*. When you say you are proud of something or someone for achieving something, that isn't a sin. C. S. Lewis described this kind of pride as warm-hearted admiration.[5] This is how you ought to feel when you achieve something remarkable. As long as you understand that it was ultimately God who gave you the gifts you have and that your devotion to God is more important than your abilities, having confidence and feeling good about your abilities is not wrong.

Vanity is a variation of moral pride. This is excessive admiration of one's own appearances or achievements. And this is what people often accuse bodybuilders of. They see them posing in the mirror and obsessing over every striation in their muscle fibers. It is certainly true that at some point, bodybuilding can become vain, and it is perhaps especially easy for bodybuilders to become vain, but I don't think that is inherently the case. Humans have shown warm-hearted admiration for their God-given figures for generations. An appreciation of the human figure, as well as acknowledgement of moral virtue, are not independent ideas. In fact, they may even be able to connect to one another, deepening your appreciation for both. In the first chapter I talked about the ancient Greek word *kalokagathia* to describe such an occurrence. (The word *kalokagathia* comes from the Greek words *kalós*, meaning "beautiful" or "noble," and *agathós*, meaning "good" or "virtuous." Together, these words encompass the idea of an individual who is both physically attractive and morally upright.)

The capacity to appreciate beauty is one of the many things that make us human and distinct from animals. That isn't insignificant. Beauty is what inspires us to reach for that which is above us. The point at which it becomes vanity isn't exactly clear and depends on the individual, but I do not think vanity is necessarily inherent to bodybuilding or sports.

2. Temperance

Another virtue I have learned from participation in sports is temperance. Just as Jesus practiced righteous anger in the temple, sports also provide lessons in controlled aggression. If a sportsperson is mindlessly aggressive, even if he's strong, he will be predictable and prone to mistakes. This will make him ineffective. To be effective in sports requires one to be aggressive but not unbridled. Temperance in this context means a combination of aggression and control. For example, in soccer, a player who wants to slide tackle to get the ball must do it in a delicate manner, or else he will be called for a foul. The entire sport of basketball necessitates finesse and a soft touch in order to be effective. As an athlete you must be aggressive yet still have control over yourself. This is temperance.

What about hyper-aggressive sports like boxing and football? In boxing there is a lot of technique. Your power can only be well utilized when you understand how to use it. Being blindingly aggressive will make you predictable and may potentially get you knocked out of the game. Likewise, in football there is a correct way to tackle; it's not a free for all tackling contest. Football players are big burly men, but they are in complete control of their strength. Being too aggressive won't help your team, but being too soft could leave you with broken bones and a score stacked against you. You need to be aggressive yet still have control over yourself.

3. Respect

No matter what sport you play, you will play it with people, whether those be your teammates, your sparring partner, or training with your coach. Playing with people will teach you respect for them.

Let's consider eSports as an example. I used to play Super Smash Bros. for Wii U competitively. (I'll spare you the details of my competitions, but you can watch my YouTube videos on this if you are curious.) Suffice it to say, the game was filled with many upsets. Because of this, I quickly learned to take all my opponents seriously. In order to survive, I had to assume they were all very competent and not to be taken for granted. Respecting the efforts, talents, and skills of other players will help you play a better game.

4. Charity

In his book *Wild at Heart*, John Eldridge recounts a story where a young man came to him angry and frustrated with his father who was his coach and a church leader. He was a basketball player, and his team had made the city finals. On the night of his big game, as he was heading out the door, his father stopped him to give him a pre-game speech. No, he didn't talk about how he needs to go out there, dig deep, bring his best game, and win. He said, "Now don't go out there and 'kick butt'—that's just not a nice thing to do."[6] Some Christians feel squeamish at the idea of competition and domination. It goes against their reputation of being nice and friendly. More foundationally, I believe their opposition to sports and competition is fundamentally rooted in their (mis)conception of charity, which has to do with sacrificing something of value to lift others up. It's a redistributive act where someone graciously gives up something of worth for the benefit of others.

In sports, I could stretch that to say that what coaches give to their players is a type of charity. Coaches provide guidance, sacrificing their time and effort to help their team. So yes, you could call that an act of charity. Concomitant to sports, however, is competition. Competition can be seen as antithetical to charity. It is a zero-sum game, where if you are winning, your opponent is necessarily losing. Therefore, to win, you must actively and intentionally work against them and not with them; you must try to oppress them, not bring them up. To actively increase the disparity between the winners and the losers. This would seem to be antithetical to Christian teachings. If we are being charitable indeed, we should not be beating down on people but bringing them up. But does this really apply to sports? Are your opponents to be considered poor? Are they to be objects of your charity? That would seem to me to be a far-stretch application of the principles of charity.

Being competitive is not anti-Christian or uncharitable. Jesus himself was often in confrontation with religious leaders and actively confronted the evil forces of the world. So in a way, being competitive in sports is compatible with Christian character and prepares you for future spiritual battles.

Sportsmanship

Beyond these considerations, we actually have a word for virtuous athletes. It's called sportsmanship. Sportsmanship is understanding that although we are in a competition, we choose to be virtuous and to give our opponent the respect they are due. With this in mind, it is often *more* sportsmanlike to play competitively. Do your opponents want to have fun, or are they competitive? If the latter, then your decision to forego kindness and aggressively play to win is actually *more* virtuous. It is a sign of respect. You are saying that you respect your opponent's desires, skills, and efforts and are willing to take them seriously. Competition brings both parties to a significantly higher level of competence than before their engagement by inspiring the best from both parties. So in a way, you actually are helping them by being more competitive.

It's also way more fun this way.

CHAPTER 3
Fitness as Intended

────◇×────

The child grew and became strong; he was filled with wisdom,
and the grace of God was on him.
–Luke 2:40

Love the Lord your God with all your heart and with all your soul
and with all your mind and with all your strength.
–Mark 12:30

One question I think is worth pondering is whether Jesus or anyone else in the Bible was muscular or if they even took physical fitness seriously. If you look directly at the texts in the Bible, you won't find much of anything regarding Jesus's physical fitness because it's a spiritual account of His life and ministry. To answer this question, therefore, we must extrapolate from elsewhere.

Jesus on Steroids?

Let us take a step back to consider what the common Jew looked like at that time and apply it to Jesus. In those days, unlike now, there weren't polarized body types because the diet was limited, and physical labor was normal and universal. Therefore, it would be safe to assume that almost everyone had a relatively similar body type.

Part of the reason people are gaining weight today is because they don't have to do many physical activities. This is one reason why gyms are necessary for our generation. Intense "workouts" equate to what used to be an expected and necessary part of life two thousand years ago, from physical labor, to performing everyday necessities, to walking everywhere on foot. So what was the average stature of a man in that time? Due to their daily routines, the average person back then was at around the same level of fitness as a moderately well-trained athlete today. Have you ever seen anyone out of shape in hunter-gatherer societies? In every story, in every legend, in every folk tale, in every drawing, they were all well-built. There was relatively minor physical divergence. Some were more slender, some were more bulky, but all were in good shape. We know that throughout history, men were either hunting (which required adept physical strength and endurance), farming (which also required a lot of manual exertion), building, or were professionally engaged in other handy work. Every job required physical effort for long periods of time, thereby building solid muscles in the workers. Sitting in an office and working day in and day out is a completely modern phenomenon for humans.

As for Jesus, He was a stonemason and a carpenter. Part of His work was lifting wood, lifting stone, and swinging a hammer. It would be hard to partake in that line of work without gaining some muscle. He also spent a lot of His ministry days walking from town to town. Luke 4:44 talks about how Jesus preached in the synagogues of Galilee. If we assume it was all over Galilee, then he walked approximately 470 kilometers (292 miles squared). So in all likelihood, Jesus would be about as muscular as an average manual labor worker. Probably not refined like a model or bodybuilder, but certainly sturdy and in good shape.

Then consider the physical and mental brutality He endured before He died. In 1986, the *Journal of the American Medical Association* published an article titled "On the Physical Death of Jesus Christ." It details the entire process of Jesus' trial to His death on the cross. In Luke 22:44, it is written that Jesus was in such great anguish that he began sweating blood while praying. Jesus, knowing everything, was filled with such overwhelming anxiety that he began to literally sweat blood. This is a condition recognized as hematidrosis, caused by such a high stress level that blood hemorrhages into the sweat glands. Before being nailed, He endured whipping by a short leather whip that would have had iron balls and sheep bones attached to the ends of the lashes. The balls caused internal injuries while the bones ripped open His flesh. After this, He had to carry a 165 lb (75 kg) cross for 600 m (0.37 miles). Due to blood loss and shock, most men would have died at this point, but this was just the build-up to the actual crucifixion. While on the cross, He had a crown of thorns piercing His scalp to the skull and nails as long as eight inches hammered into his wrists and ankles. After this, He had a spear pierced to his side.[1] Isaiah 52:14 says His body was "disfigured beyond that of any man." We have an entire word, "excruciating," to describe exactly what He graciously endured for our sake before and while He was on the cross. He sacrificed that body to show just how much He loved us.

One would need to be very fit and extremely strong to endure what Jesus did—well beyond ordinary human capacity. So my answer to the question of whether Jesus was fit is a resounding *yes*, He absolutely was. It turns out our God is really strong. Man shall not live on bread alone, it doesn't have enough protein.

Christians and Fitness

In the later part of the nineteenth century in the United States, churches started to push back on the idea that God doesn't want us to exercise. Christians began changing their understanding of the sanctity of the body and consequently of sports and exercise. Liberal theologians led the way to this reversal. Colleges began to see aggressiveness in sports as a way of training men and women for the many challenges of life, drawing analogies to real-life issues and building virtues that would help young people to cope and to attain spiritual heights.[2]

Because of advances in technology, our generation doesn't see the immediate importance of personal physical fitness. We have developed new technologies for every laborious work, and we can rely on heavy medication to stay healthy. We don't need cardiovascular endurance because we have cars, and we don't bother with strength training because we have machines to carry things for us.

On top of this, every so often we are bombarded on social media with before-and-after photos of people going on extreme diets and losing weight, and we are told these new fad diets are the way to do it. This was especially the case back in the early 2010s when young girls seemed to be obsessed with the idea of being as thin as possible. The fact that they might have been hurting themselves with their extreme diets did not seep into their consciousness. This idea doesn't seem to be as popular now, but the ethos around it still rings strong. Its embers still linger around.

There are others who, in their bid to become like their heroes on social media, take copious amounts of performance-enhancing drugs for prolonged periods of time. Many only succeed in destroying their bodies and jeopardizing their health. This is not fitness, but rather a grossly misconstrued attempt at mimicking idols through bodily disfigurement. Doing this pushes your body to such unnatural extremes and makes it more about maximizing performance in a specific field than about improving the holistic functions of the human body.

Strength, aesthetics, and health are often linked, but they aren't the same. To push yourself to such extremes would reduce your body's ability to survive. This goes against the *telos* (proper end) of your body's functions. Thus it goes against what it means to be fit. To be fit is to improve an organism's ability to survive, and this is what happens when the body is functioning at maximum capacity.

Fitness isn't necessarily about having big, strong muscles or about having the most attractive figure; it is about having a maximally functional body. This means that it isn't just about being healthy *enough*, it is about being exceptional and pristine. We don't look at someone who is average and say that they are fit; instead, we look at someone with good cardiovascular endurance, muscle strength, flexibility, and explosiveness and say that they are fit. These faculties together, not individually, make someone fit. This is not to be confused with athleticism, which is purely about performance. Athleticism may be a fun and healthy pursuit, but it is not synonymous with fitness. If there were a Venn Diagram laying athletics and fitness over one another, they would overlap a lot, but not completely.

Excessive muscle size and cardiovascular endurance can actually make you less fit. When you develop one faculty of fitness to the significant detriment of all the other faculties, you are, on the net, making yourself less functional and therefore less fit. For example, if you do so much cardio to the point where your bones become weak, you have ironically become less fit in your pursuit of fitness. You have hindered the organism's ability to survive. Not only can this cause osteoporosis in women, but it will also significantly reduce muscle strength. Strong muscles are a natural and necessary function of the human person. You can think of it as a math equation: If you gain 100 percent endurance without the detriment of anything else, you are more fit. But if you gain 110 percent endurance and lose 20 percent muscle strength in pursuit of that extra 10 percent, you have become less fit overall. This doesn't even take into account the other health issues that arise when you go below your baseline level of functioning, such as the aforementioned osteoporosis.

Fitness is strengthening your body or restoring your body to what it ought to be. That way it can function maximally. One of our principal duties as Christians is to serve and help one another. In order to do this effectively, we need to be available physically, mentally, and spiritually. We love God spiritually, mentally, and physically. We love the Lord with all our heart, soul, mind, *and* strength. God has given each of us a body; let us take care of it. By doing so, we will glorify Him. Then when our earthly body is ultimately taken away, it will be perfected and made glorious in heaven.

Functional Training

In this discussion of what it means to be fit, I believe it is worth discussing what has been dubbed "functional training" by fitness influencers. The actual definition is extremely vague. Some people say it means to train natural, primal movements; some people say that it means to only train calisthenics; and some people say that it means to train on a Bosu Ball. In my view, functional training, if it means anything, is to optimize the functions of our body. *All* functions of our body. This seems to be a fundamental appeal to natural law. Natural law is a moral philosophy coined by people like Aristotle, the apostle Paul, and Thomas Aquinas. It more or less means that we know right and wrong based on the natural law written on our hearts. That's very oversimplified, but it will work for our discussion.

Within natural law, there is a natural order. Natural order in this context essentially means that we should acknowledge our natural design in everything we do. With this in mind, functional training attempts to promote a way of exercising in such a way that our body is naturally designed to move. Your body is made for food—to process it, digest it, break it down, convert it into energy. Likewise, our muscles are made for various purposes. This includes, but isn't limited to, pulling yourself up, squatting, running, jumping, and picking things up off the ground (akin to deadlifting.) So with this philosophy, it makes sense that we should optimize these functions. The embedded idea behind functional training and why it appeals to so many people is because it maximizes every bodily function. Because our bodies are capable of doing something, because it is in our nature to do something, it is therefore good to optimize that natural capability. This makes it such that the highest bodily good is to optimize all the bodily functions. It's not doing calisthenics instead of weights or doing Bosu ball squats, it is holistically looking at the body, optimizing, and balancing all that it is capable of.

Functional training is philosophically conjoined with natural order, and the natural order is written on our hearts. This is likely why people gravitate toward it. (As an aside, I think the more accurate way to describe this kind of training is "nature training" because it is philosophically derived from natural order. I talk about this more in chapter 15.) I am not saying that we *must* be maximally functional athletes, but I am saying that we shouldn't disregard any physical faculty. With rare exceptions, I do not believe it is good to get strong at the significant expense of flexibility or gain endurance at the significant expense of muscle. Everyone has their own natural strengths and weaknesses. It is good to play to your strengths. It is the neglect that I take issue with. Neglecting key components of your physical capacities would be wrong.

Drugs

This is a good segue to the issue of drugs, a prevailing issue in the world of sports. Although some people argue that moderate use of performance-enhancing drugs isn't sinful, I will err on the side of caution and say that performance-enhancing drugs are contrary to Christian beliefs. I personally would not feel comfortable taking them. If your body is a temple, I don't think you should be putting foreign and harmful substances into it. First, because it ultimately destroys your body; second, because they are unnatural substances that change the way your body is designed; and third, because you may be cheating your non-doping adversaries in a competition (depending on the competition), and that is immoral.

Although I am no expert on drugs, I am well read, and I can assure you that this topic is much more nuanced than it appears. You must consider the degree of consumption with the drug, how it can be moderated, and assess the associated drawbacks. You must also consider the specific drug you are talking about. Is it bioidentical like testosterone? Or is it a drug not found in the human body like trenbolone? Since trenbolone doesn't naturally exist in the human body, one may argue that adding something like that into your system is not in accordance with how God made you. Testosterone may be bioidentical, but when taken exogenously, it is considered unnatural. Testosterone may still run into *teleological* issues. Injecting extra doses that your body doesn't produce naturally will shrink a man's testicles because they are no longer required for testosterone production. In this case, one may argue that a part of your body ceases to perform the way it is meant to perform to give way to the new drugs. This level of bodily adjustment would appear sinful to a lot of people.

You also must consider how you may be impacting everyone who looks at your performance. You will have to contemplate how your actions are influencing the people in your life. Man is not an island. Your actions will either implicitly or explicitly influence and invite others to perform like you, even though *you* are not even performing like you. Some people in the bodybuilding community believe that we should be more open about drug use. However, what this will likely do implicitly is tell the people looking at your performance to hop on drugs in a bid to perform like you, all while harming their bodies in the process.

Your incredible looks and performance may have normalized the idea in their head. You may have made drug use acceptable to them. You can tell them that drug abuse is bad for their health, but if you yourself are taking it, most people will not heed your warning. People look up to you. They want to become like you. To look like you and perform like you. Part of what it takes to do that is to take drugs. If you hide your drug use or don't speak about it, the people looking up to you may become resentful at the fact that their natural bodies cannot perform the way your ostensibly natural body may be performing. It seems as though you risk either physically hurting people or psychologically hurting people. All of these are important questions and considerations if this issue personally impacts you.

Nevertheless, I believe two God-fearing Christians could have a genuine disagreement about this topic. I know some Christian athletes who think differently. I respect their opinions, but I disagree with them. I will conclude by acknowledging that this issue might be something you must ultimately defer to your own conscience. Like many things that aren't outright condemned in the Bible, the test of whether we should engage in any activity not expressly addressed is to check our regenerated consciences.

Notice that I speak of regenerated consciences, not consciences already steeped in worldliness, or in the present-day cultural norms, which do not align with Christian beliefs. Romans 14:22–23 explains that if you have doubts about doing something, then it's best not to do it, regardless of its legality. If you're fully confident something isn't a sin, you're good. But if you're not sure, yet do it anyway in the hopes it is not a sin, it becomes a sin for you, even if it isn't a sin for others. This is because your conscience has warned you not to do it. This is how Paul addresses this among believers, using the conflict of whether to eat meat that has been offered to idols. Romans 14:22–23, "So whatever you believe about these things keep it between yourself and God. Blessed is the one who does not condemn himself by what he approves. But whoever has doubts is condemned if they eat, because their eating is not from faith; and everything that does not come from faith is sin."

CHAPTER 4
Deadly Sins

━━━━━━━━━━━━━━━━━━━━━❮ ❯━━━━━━━━━━━━━━━━━━━━━

No one can serve two masters. Either you will hate the one and love the other,
or you will be devoted to the one and despise the other.
–Matthew 6:24

The seven deadly sins are rooted in Roman Catholicism. The list is made up of the following vices: pride, greed, lust, envy, gluttony, wrath, and sloth. Each of the deadly sins can be overcome by the corresponding virtues of humility, charity, chastity, gratitude, temperance, patience, and diligence.

Gluttony and sloth are the two I will discuss here because they are the most intimately linked to our health, and both can be cured or curbed by exercise and physical activity. Gluttony refers to over-indulgence to the point that it becomes detrimental; sloth has to do with laziness and inactivity, also to the point that it becomes detrimental to a person's health and well-being.

Gluttony

Gluttony is overindulgence in food or drinks, although the word can be extended to include just about anything we indulge in. It is giving way to your appetite instead of giving to your body what it is due. Gluttony could include any form of addiction. My focus, however, will be on food and drinks.

In the Bible, we read in Proverbs 23:19–21, "Listen, my son, and be wise, and set your heart on the right path: Do not join those who drink too much wine or gorge themselves on meat, for drunkards and gluttons become poor, and drowsiness clothes them in rags."

This verse is complemented by Ecclesiastes 10:17, "Blessed is the land whose king is of noble birth and whose princes eat at a proper time—for strength and not for drunkenness."

From these two verses we learn that first, we shouldn't drink too much; and second, when we do eat or drink, we should do it at the proper time. Not following these instructions is a path to gluttony. Gluttony is caused not just by how much you indulge but also by when you indulge.

From the list of the vices and the virtues, we can see that the sin of gluttony is counterbalanced by the virtue of temperance. C. S. Lewis describes temperance as "not abstaining, but going the right length and no further."[1]

The ability to control gluttony necessarily requires one to cultivate discipline. On this issue, the mind, the body, and the spirit are once more in metaphysical synergy. They are connected. Training your mind to resist the temptations of gluttony will help your body stay healthy and your soul stay clean. Temperance in the ingestion of physical substances encourages physical, mental, and spiritual growth.

Temperance is not to be confused with abstinence. Abstinence is a complete withdrawal from vice. It hinges on the idea that something is bad and should never be indulged in. Examples include some of the behaviors that the Bible forbids as being morally reprehensible, such as pornography or sex before marriage. Or it could be things that are harmful to an individual's health. A drunkard is someone who is addicted to alcohol. He is not indulging in something that in itself is bad, but is only bad because he has no control over his desire. All he needs to go down a downward spiral is just one sip of liquor. For the drunkard, therefore, his only choice is to completely abstain.

Sloth

A sloth is an animal that is named after one of the deadly sins. It has become so synonymous with laziness that it is referred to as a state of being. A sloth is the slowest mammal in the world moving at a blistering top speed of 0.27km/h (0.17mph) when threatened.[2] They stay on their own all day and all night. They are said to have also been genetically adapted to be able to sleep while hanging from trees.

Sloth is the lack of any inclination, expression, or discipline. It's an extreme case of laziness, a form that is incapable of moving fast. It is a laziness within its habitat that has adapted to a lifestyle of inaction. Similar to a real sloth, it is as though the slothful person has engineered a lazy life for themselves through their ecosystem. In the Bible, Paul speaks very negatively of those who don't do anything, even asserting that if you don't work you shouldn't eat (2 Thessalonians 3:10).

Mark 14 gives an account of the disciples' lack of discipline in the final hours leading to Jesus' crucifixion. He took Peter, James, and John to the Garden of Gethsemane to pray. When they got there, He told the disciples to stay a short distance from Him and to keep watch. Before He could finish one round of prayer, the disciples had slept off. Sloth is when we know we should be doing something, and we aren't doing it. Perhaps it's because we don't see it as important. The disciples didn't see this small task as important. But everything, even the things you think are insignificant, can be very important. To reach the top level in sports requires meticulous attention to detail. This is why sports teams look back on the film footage from their previous games to discern what they did well and what they can improve upon. Every small detail matters.

Jesus asked the disciples to do this simple job because if they could properly do it to the best of their ability, if they would take care in doing little things perfectly, they would be better prepared to do the more important assignments. He was preparing them for the more difficult tasks they would be entrusted with later in their lives.

Retired United States Navy officer Jocko Willink speaks of a similar experience after his promotion in the navy. He said,

> When I got done with Basic SEAL Training and reported on board SEAL Team One, you know what I was assigned to do? I was assigned to clean toilets. That's right—despite having just graduated [from] some of the most difficult military training in the world, despite being assigned to an "elite" commando unit—my first mission at the actual SEAL Team was to clean toilets. Not exactly a glorious job. But you know what? I did it. I did it to the best of my ability and took pride in doing it well. And that attitude got noticed: if I cared that much about how clean the toilets were, people knew I would do a good job with even more important assignments. After a short period of time, I got those more important assignments. But it was humility that opened the door for me.[3]

Diligence is the accompanying virtue countering sloth. Diligence requires discipline. To be responsible requires discipline. One of the reasons that exercise relates to self-improvement is because it instills discipline. As explained in the first chapter, there may be no reason your body has to exercise right now. Yet you are forcing it to. Everything in your body may be telling you not to do it, that you can put it off until the next day, and that you should save your energy. But you know that you should be doing it. So you make a habit of doing it. You want to be consistent. To be consistent in doing things even when you aren't motivated requires discipline.

Your walk with God follows a similar trajectory. One missed day turns into six more. One missed church service turns into ten missed services, which eventually changes your lifestyle. Your mind needs to be strong enough to force your body to move when your body is protesting. Your mind must be strong enough to train your spirit. If you do not intentionally and actively discipline your body, mind, and spirit, you may gradually slip into any of the seven deadly sins.

CHAPTER 5

I'm Here for a Good Time—and a Long Time and a Meaningful Time

———————————<×>———————————

*Consider it pure joy, my brothers and sisters, whenever you face trials of many
kinds, because you know that the testing of your faith produces perseverance.
Let perseverance finish its work so that you may be mature and complete,
not lacking anything.*

—James 1:2–4

*If one accomplishes some good though with toil, the toil passes
but the good remains; if one does something dishonorable with pleasure,
the pleasure passes, but the dishonor remains.*

—Musonius Rufus

*I denied myself nothing my eyes desired; I refused my heart no pleasure.
My heart took delight in all my labor, and this was the reward for all my toil.
Yet when I surveyed all that my hands had done and what I had toiled to achieve,
everything was meaningless, a chasing after the wind;
nothing was gained under the sun.*

—Ecclesiastes 2:10–11

*Far and away the best prize that life offers is
the chance to work hard at work worth doing.*

—Theodore Roosevelt

There is a phrase spoken by many in this generation. It's credited to
the country singer George Strait in his song "Here for a Good
Time."[1] However, it was made famous by the rapper Big Sean in his
song "Blessings,"[2] which features Drake, another popular artist. In the
chorus, Drake sings, "I'm here for a good time, *not a long time.*" This

phrase is emblematic of how my generation thinks. Drake is their mouthpiece.

Perhaps if you're an atheist who doesn't believe in the afterlife, I can see how you could develop the mentality of Drake's words. A pleasurable, short life sounds better than a dreadful, long life. This could make a lot of sense for anyone with a purely materialistic worldview. Under this worldview, you are left with two end results: (1) Prolong this life as long as possible as this is the only one you will ever have (a long time). (2) Completely disregard your physical well-being, pursue superficial pleasure, and live for the now (a good time).

I believe there is a third option, not mentioned in the original phrase, that can result from atheism. One where people, in effect; create a god of their own to worship. We saw this a lot in the twentieth century with the rise of communism and fascism. People did inconceivable things in the name of their secular ideologies and enacted fascist and communist policies. People effectively worshiped the state. This is what the atheist German philosopher Friedrich Nietzsche worried about when he claimed, "God is dead. God remains dead. And we have killed him." However, I don't want to focus on that point for this book. I want to focus on the worldviews espoused by Drake.

Most atheists don't fully act within the assumptions of options 1 and 2, probably because they haven't contemplated their mortality, certainly not to the point where they ponder how they should live their lives given their philosophical framework. It could also be that they have thought about it and chosen to simply ignore it. And this may be for the best. If you subscribe to the first option, you may end up realizing that death as a portal into a black, empty abyss of nothingness and that all of you will ultimately be erased from this world. This is possibly how Nietzsche felt. He went mad after allegedly seeing a horse being whipped. (Nietzsche coddled a horse being beaten down despite the fact that it went against the ethos of his master and slave morality ideology. More on that in chapter 13). His worldview resulted in a crippling and incapacitating fear of death.

If you primarily subscribe to the latter option, you may come to the conclusion that nothing in your life matters; and therefore, there is no point in even trying to make anything of it. You accept the fact that when you die, you will be eaten by bugs, that nothing you do will ever make any significant impact on the world, and you will never be remembered for anything. So then, instead of living in fear, give in to any cravings that come your way. Eat, drink, party, try drugs—YOLO! (You Only Live Once!). Do whatever you want and whatever you think will give you the greatest pleasure. When you get rid of God, there is no solid foundation for morality—thus no morality, only preferences. If there is no right and wrong, then everything is permissible. There is no basis to say that anything is wrong. Society becomes a cacophonous playground where things might temporarily work, but ultimately everyone's capricious desires reign supreme, with no objective reference point to distinguish right from wrong. To have a functional society, people with this worldview add a caveat saying that they will do whatever they want *as long as it doesn't directly hurt other people.* This leads to a society of people stuck in a secluded hedonic treadmill of dopamine loops. People will temporarily numb themselves to the banality of a meaningless life by seeking novel forms of pleasure.

The option 2 mentality, when widely adopted, creates a society that only cares for itself. They care only for living in the moment and satisfying their immediate desires. A society that is only concerned about itself is, by definition, not concerned with the future. A society that has no concern for the future is a society that will die. A selfish life will ultimately leave no impact on the wider society. That person will use up resources, die, and disappear, leaving nothing to show for his existence. In this materialist worldview, taking your time to draw a beautiful piece of art is the metaphysical equivalent to getting drunk or high. Nothing has any higher value. It's all relative. It's all just a bunch of chemicals moving around at the end of the day. Who cares? According to this philosophy, if life is only for short-term pleasure, why not lie, cheat, and steal? There is no compelling reason not to live with complete self-interest. There is no objective benefit to being a good person. Particularly if the opposite makes you feel better. In this ultimately meaningless universe, what difference would anything make? Reality is completely arbitrary. Who cares about pointless things like truth in this indifferent universe? Especially if that truth is inconvenient to our immediate satisfaction. We all just came into being due to some supernatural fluke. Even if one does inspire positive change, it won't last. History is cyclical. We may as well have the most fun we can while we are still alive.

This philosophy is getting stronger and more widespread adoption in the western world as many continue to write God out of their lives and are focusing instead on themselves. While the atheist cannot fully live like this, the belief in this worldview still lives out in small ways that lead to negative outcomes, which we will talk about later.

Atheists of the early centuries actually agreed with this worldview. Jean-Paul Satre, an existentialist and atheist philosopher said that the atheistic philosophy was "cruel business" and is famous for claiming that "life is absurd."[3] Similarly, the atheist philosopher Bertrand Russel even admitted that despite his strong opposition to theism and his devotion to atheism, he could not live out the atheist worldview and that consequently, he lived as though there were a God.[4] The cheerful atheism of Richard Dawkins and Sam Harris is logically inconsistent and fails to comprehend the radical consequences of the rejection of God. To reject God is to untether the earth from its orbit around the sun.

To drift aimlessly in the hollow void of endless space. The atheists of the early centuries were more honest in their assessment of their worldview. They knew that they could not fully uproot the edifice of God in their hearts, but they also did not want to ultimately submit to God which created an uncomfortable cognitive dissonance.

Some may argue that life's impermanence actually gives life more meaning. The fact that you only have a small amount of time makes everything you do more impactful. Think about it like someone who knows he is going to die in the next month and creates a bucket list of things he will do before he dies. This will make every remaining moment more meaningful.

But this creates another problem in the long run. If everything you do now has ultimate meaning, then logically speaking, every moment you are not making the most of your time or doing the most meaningful thing, you are wasting. And you will never have that time back. You could theoretically be doing something more meaningful than reading this book. But you aren't. Therefore, you are wasting time that you will never get back. This may cycle you back to the former problem, where you have an immobilizing fear of death as you will be missing out on something meaningful that you could be doing.

The atheist, again, cannot logically live out his philosophy without going insane. If you do believe in God, you will do what you think is meaningful now, but also understand that even if you aren't always doing everything optimally, you have a whole afterlife to look forward to. You can enjoy this life but understand there is another one waiting.

Suffering and Reward

Perhaps due to understanding the end result of their worldview, some atheists have something insightful to say about the problem of suffering. According to Nietzsche, life is suffering. Nevertheless, what is found through suffering is true joy. It is only through surviving hard times that a deeper joy is created. He said, "The meaninglessness of suffering, not suffering itself, is the curse that lies over mankind."[5] Meaningless suffering is torture, but suffering itself isn't necessarily a bad thing if it is in service to a higher good. By giving up something in the present, we may obtain a better future. Nietzsche also said, "What if pleasure and displeasure were so tied together that whoever wanted to have as much as possible of one must also have as much as possible of the other—that whoever wants to learn to 'jubilate up to the heavens' must also be prepared for 'grief unto death'?"[6] You have a choice in how you want to live life—either as little displeasure as possible, painlessness in brief, or as much displeasure as possible and enjoy your lasting reward later. I will voice my disagreements with Nietzsche later in the book, but to great extent, I do agree with what he said about suffering.

Humans do not develop without strain. The mind develops greater endurance, moral fiber, understanding, and depth through the stress of trials and struggles in life. The mind that never endures any discomfort or trouble will, in all likelihood, crumble when real, prolonged stress is applied.

All of this is analogous to exercise. You go through pain, destroying your muscles, only to have them come back stronger. If I were to ask someone running on a treadmill right at this moment, if they were happy, they would probably tell me that they aren't. In fact, they might tell me they're miserable. If I were to ask someone who is drinking soda, eating chips, and binging the latest Netflix series if they are happy, they will probably say that, of course, they're happy. But we all know which activity is more beneficial in the end. The one whose activity will end up giving back to him in the form of physical benefits that can impact the rest of his life is the one on the treadmill. Very soon he will begin to enjoy running, he may even achieve a "runners high," a phrase describing the state of euphoria when running. Being healthy is something you will ultimately enjoy once you make exercising and healthy eating a habit. These things quickly become sustainable pleasures. The one binging on Netflix, if nothing is changed and if it consumes the bulk of their time, will become unhealthy and lazy. They will begin to hate it but find it difficult to change.

Christianity is similar. Practicing virtue and living for God is difficult in the short term, but in the long term, it is infinitely rewarding. Living in vice may seem like the easy, quick, and simple solution, but this ultimately leads to misery.

No discipline seems pleasant at the time, but painful. Later on, however,
it produces a harvest of righteousness and peace for those who have been trained by it.
Therefore, strengthen your feeble arms and weak knees.

–Hebrews 12:11–12

Anything that is worthwhile and excellent takes time, discipline, and sacrifice. And human beings are naturally wired to aspire toward that which demonstrates it. We watch Michael Jordan glide across the court with his forty-six-inch vertical and are inspired to "Be like Mike!" We know there is sacrifice in that and ultimately understand just how rewarding it all is. In the documentary *The Last Dance*, one of Jordan's college teammates, James Worthy, spoke about how hard Michael Jordan worked to achieve all that he did. He said "After about 2.5 hours of hard practice, I'm walking off the floor, like, drenched [in] sweat, tired. And here comes Michael pushing me back on the floor, wanting to play a little one-on-one, wanting to see where his game was."[7] Ultimately, all this sacrifice and hard work was worth it as Michael Jordan became one of, if not the greatest basketball player of all time.

On this note, Theodore Roosevelt's speech *The Strenuous Life* promotes the embrace of an active and challenging existence. He said,

> I wish to preach, not the doctrine of ignoble ease, but the doctrine of the strenuous life. The life of toil and effort, of labor gold strife; to preach that highest form of success which comes, not to the man who desires mere easy peace, but to the man who does not shrink from danger, from hardship or from bitter toil, and who out of these wins the splendid ultimate triumph. . . . though [you] may have leisure, it is not to be spent in idleness; for wisely used leisure merely means that those who possess it, being free from the necessity of working for their livelihood, are all the more bound to carry on some kind of non-remunerative work in science, in letters, in art, in exploration, in historical research-work of the type we most need in this country, the successful carrying out of which reflects most honor upon the nation.[8]

Pursue excellence through suffering because that's where true joy and greatness is found. To live "for a good time," therefore, would be to reject the pursuit of true excellence and focus on your own pleasures.

The question of a good time versus a long time actually posits a false dichotomy. The Christian life calls us not to necessarily live for a good time or a long time but rather for a meaningful time. Prolonging life for its own sake at the detriment of spiritual fulfillment is not what I am promoting. I am also not promoting destroying your body because your time on Earth is short in the face of eternity. I am advocating for everyone to live life in pursuit of physical and spiritual excellence. Atheists acknowledge that there is no objective meaning to life; Christians live to bring glory to God above all and to serve humanity. We serve best when we are physically and spiritually strong and healthy.

It is theorized that only one of Jesus's eleven disciples died of natural causes. That one exception was John, who lived a full and meaningful life and later died of natural causes as an old man. The rest were martyred. They died willingly because they answered the call to serve Christ. They believed in, and committed themselves to, this call even when they knew it could cost them their lives. While dying, they were more alive than they ever could have imagined. They found transcendent joy in fulfilling their life's purpose even though their calling sent them to an early grave. They lived to spread the truth. Not *their* truth. Not *some* truth. Not *a* truth. But *the* Truth.

We should accept that our physical life is temporary and will eventually pass away. We should live knowing that all our earthly possessions and all our earthly achievements will also pass away. We should not obsess about extending our lives; we should also not waste it meaninglessly. We must find a balance. While we do our best to promote a healthy life, we must also be prepared to take calculated and reasonable risks. Take care of your body and keep it in good shape, but bear in mind that it can be taken from you at any time. Challenge yourself to live a meaningful, purposeful life. This will bring richness, fullness, and wholeness to you.

The life we live on earth is just a blink compared to the life after, which is eternal and will never end. Taking care of the body we've been given in this life is the right way to extend our lives, to live it with purpose, and to live it fulfilled. I desire to live to a ripe old age. I desire to be able to dance with my spouse well into our old age. I desire to live long enough to see and play with my grandchildren, and perhaps my great-grandchildren. I desire to live a full life, to work hard, to contribute to my generation, to see the fruit of my labor, to leave this world a better place than I found it, even if it is only in some infantile way. I don't want to live a life that is focused on the fear of dying. I want to take care of myself well enough so I can enjoy my life. I want my life to be infused with Jesus, so I can live passionately and without fear.

If you agree with me, you will also agree that one of the best ways to live such a life is to treat the body He gave you as the wonderful temple it is. Take care of it and keep it well-tended for the sake of yourself, for others, and for God's glory.

At milestone birthdays, we often wish the celebrant "a good life and a long life." A good life is a meaningful life; a long life is a healthy life. The two ought to go hand in hand for full satisfaction.

Consider Paul's dilemma about life and death in his letter to the Philippians. He wrote this toward the end of his life:

> For to me, to live is Christ and to die is gain. If I am to go on living in the body, this will mean fruitful labor for me. Yet what shall I choose? I do not know! I am torn between the two: I desire to depart and be with Christ, which is better by far; but it is more necessary for you that I remain in the body. Convinced of this, I know that I will remain, and I will continue with all of you for your progress and joy in the faith, so that through my being with you again your boasting in Christ Jesus will abound on account of me. (Philippians 1:21–26)

A good time and a long time are not inversely correlated but positively correlated. When you focus on your health, you are actually living for a good time *and* a long time. A combination of physical and spiritual health is what you need for total health. Other ingredients of a good and long time on earth, also recognized by secular psychologists and social scientists, include good and intimate relationships with your friends, marital partner, as well as with your parents and siblings.[9]

Spiritual fulfillment is another element that correlates to a longer life. God gave us spirituality; it seems to come naturally to humans and sets us apart from other creatures. Research has shown again and again that there is indeed a relationship between religious participation and mental well-being regardless of social support or financial status.[10] Such benefits aren't emulated by just being spiritual and/or having a robust community. They are unique to the religious life.

It is incredibly reassuring to me to see that in a Gallup poll, the only group of people whose mental health wasn't negatively impacted by COVID were regular churchgoers.[11] It would seem, therefore, that infusing meaning to life in those trying times did absolute wonders for your mental health, curbing the effects of a bleak news cycle and physical lockdowns.

Christians also have the happiest marriages.[11] Their marriages aren't oriented towards fulfilling the individual feelings of each member; they are oriented towards a higher purpose. They point towards something outside and above themselves. They answer to a higher authority which instills a level of humility in the spouses. They realize they are not the ones ultimately in charge. They are not making it up or winging it as they go. They have roles. They have their house built on solid rock and not on sand.

It is important to note that all these benefits come from being intrinsically, not extrinsically, Christian. Intrinsic Christianity means that you internally believe that the religion is part of you, whereas extrinsic religiosity means that you just follow a bunch of routines because of culture or tradition. Extrinsic Christians see God as a means, intrinsic Christians see God as the end. Extrinsic Christianity uses God for what they want instead of loving Him for who He is. It isn't enough to mentally assent to the idea of a God; you have to fully devote your life to Him.

Although we earlier discussed the disciples of Jesus who died young, both the Bible and present-day society are full of people to whom God gave long and happy lives. But no matter how long you live, God wants you to take care of the physical body He has given you, so you can be fruitful and productive for Him. Your physical health is your responsibility. How can you be sure that you can enjoy a meaningful life, serving God your friends and your family to the fullest? The machine in which you can experience that fulfillment is your body. Therefore, we should all attend to our physical health.

CHAPTER 6
Exercise and the Good Life

———————————— ✕ ◇ ✕ ————————————

In order for man to succeed in life, God provided him with two means—education
and physical activity. Not separately, one for the soul and the other for the body,
but for the two together. With these means, man can attain perfection.

–Plato

So far, we have established that the mind and the body are connected and actively complement each other. They cannot be compartmentalized. The top-ten causes of death, according to the CDC, are heart disease, cancer, accidental injuries, chronic lower respiratory disease, stroke, Alzheimer's disease, diabetes, influenza, kidney disease, and suicide.[1] Throw in a cheeky stat about how overweight people are at a higher risk of injuries, and I can say the top ten causes of death are highly correlated with a lack of exercise, being overweight, being sad/depressed, or a combination of the three.[2]

Exercise has been shown to directly improve long term mental health, curb stress and anxiety, and help people overcome addiction. Exercise also fosters community spirit via team sports, which are all very important for our well-being. All of this is a circuitous way to say that exercise could aid in reducing the magnitude of the suicide epidemic, meaning that exercise can actually have a direct impact on all the previously mentioned top-ten causes of death. Truly, if there were a drug that did everything exercise did with no repercussions, it would be the most valuable item on the planet. So why isn't everyone "lining up" to "buy" this "drug?" In this chapter, we explore some of the ways exercise affects our health.

Exercise and Stress

As explained in the first chapter, human beings are physically hard-wired to constantly move about and exercise. Every day, we build up a lot of stress, and physical exercise provides an outlet to get this out of our system so we can stay healthy. In the modern world, our stress is exacerbated by our incessant consumption of negative news and by rapid changes in our culture and norms. Negativity and confusion add stress to the body. Exercise will help manage this by releasing neuro-transmitters, called endorphins, into our body to manage our response.

Exercise temporarily mimics the fight-or-flight response that you may feel when you are stressed. But in the long run, it will help calm and de-stress you. Endorphins help calm your responses and ultimately result in removing the built-up stresses from our lives. Studies have shown that people experience positive changes after just one or two cardio sessions. Exercise will also help you sleep, which is directly correlated with lower stress and anxiety.[3]

Exercise and Anxiety

Exercise helps you decrease your levels of general and social anxiety. Nearly one in eight adults and one in three teenagers will reportedly experience a chronic anxiety disorder sometime in their life.[4] People who report high levels of physical activity are better protected against developing anxiety symptoms compared to those who report low levels of physical activity. According to the Harvard Medical School,

- Engaging in exercise diverts you from the very thing you are anxious about.

- Moving your body decreases muscle tension and lowers the body's contribution to feeling anxious.

- Getting your heart rate up changes your brain chemistry, increasing the availability of important anti-anxiety neurochemicals, including serotonin, gamma aminobutyric acid (GABA), brain-derived neurotrophic factor (BDNF), and endocannabinoids.

- Exercise activates frontal regions of the brain responsible for executive function, which helps control the amygdala, our reacting system to real or imagined threats to our survival.

- Exercising regularly builds up resources that bolster resilience against stormy emotions.[5]

Exercise and Addiction

This may seem weird, but exercise can help you reclaim your body and help you recover from addiction and curb your cravings. When you get off an addiction, your body will go through withdrawal symptoms. You may get irritable and anxious. This is because your body misses the high feelings it used to get.

Conveniently, exercise helps with anxiety. It does this by calming your brain down and putting it in a pseudo-meditative state. When you exercise, you lose track of what was irritating you before your workout. You concentrate solely on your body's movements. I notice this is especially the case when doing aerobic exercise like playing a sport or running.

Exercise releases feel-good chemicals into your system. Exercise increases oxytocin, which is responsible for feeling connected with other people. One of the worst parts of addiction is the feeling of loneliness. Raising your oxytocin level, getting a gym partner, or shooting hoops at the local park will go a long way to making you feel connected and to (potentially) establish friendships. Taking care of yourself and maintaining close relationships isn't always easy or fun. You may not reap results early, but the ultimate results will pay off, making it worth every sweat.[6]

Part II:
Your Body for God's Glory

CHAPTER 7
Fitness Idolatry

Everyone who competes in the games goes into strict training. They do it to get a crown that will not last, but we do it to get a crown that will last forever.
–1 Corinthians 9:25

I can do all this through him who gives me strength.
–Philippians 4:13

If seeds in the black earth can turn into such beautiful roses, what might not the heart of man become in its long journey toward the stars?
–G. K. Chesterton

Physical strength can be a vehicle that helps us to become high achievers. However, we must not idolize our bodies, and we should not *obsessively* worry about our fitness. It is Christ who strengthens us.

Truth is, as human beings, we can never reach our ideal, or our peak, or our genetic limit. It is impossible. We can always be better than whatever point we are at now. We keep inching closer, but we will never attain the ultimate ideal; we are like an asymptote curve reaching its vanishing point. An asymptote is a line that a curve approaches and gets closer and closer to but ultimately never touches. It has no ending. Likewise, we only inch closer to our limit but never actually make it. The endpoint is ambiguous. Often, right when you think you are about to make it, you start to regress. This could be due to illness, injury, or other life circumstances. So we can only get close to our optimum but never fully hit it.

A similar idea holds true in our relationship with God. Just like being optimally fit is a never-ending target, becoming Christlike is a never-ending pursuit. In *Church of Cowards*, Matt Walsh points out that the Bible always uses the language of us *following* God.[1] There is no adjacent language used that implies that we are ever equal to Him or that we can ever stop pursuing more of Him. The implication is that we are constantly moving forward, following Him, aiming at where He may be, and that He is always ahead of us. So pace forward without stopping. You can't stay in the same place. To do so would be to be moving away from Him.

God is infinitely good and infinitely sovereign. We can never fully reach Him because we are finite creatures. Like the curve approaching the asymptote, we can never reach God. He is so far beyond us. We will never be worthy of Him and never be fully like Him. If God is the asymptote, we are the curve approaching it. As we get closer, it seems to us that He's moving infinitely further away; while we are still inching toward where we thought He was—and even then, still not reaching it. There is only a speck of God that we can comprehend. Of that speck, we have only barely filled it. In reality however, God is a cosmic oasis of infinitely expansive glory.

God's glory is like an iridescent crystal with infinite sides. When you first lift the crystal, you look at it from one angle and are made privy to His infinite majesty. Then you turn the crystal around ever so slightly to see another angle. This angle highlights another side of God's infinite glory, yet this side looks nothing like the previous side. It captures a part of God's glory from a completely different perspective. You turn the crystal again and you see a third side of God in an entirely new perspective. Completely different in kind from the first two sides. And you can continue doing this an infinite number of times.

"Obsessing" over God is a good obsession because God brings infinite fulfillment and satisfaction to our lives. You can study God philosophically, scientifically, linguistically, or sociologically, all of which bring a new perspective, all of which are infinitely fulfilling in their own right, all of which coalesce into the ultimate deity.

Fitness is not infinitely fulfilling; therefore, it ought not to be our ultimate good. This is what separates God from our earthly idols. Atheists cope with their worldview by creating their own personal meaning of life—their personal ultimate good. (In Christianity, this would be known as an idol.) Because they do not have God, the same level of fulfillment cannot be obtained. Because God is above us and is infinite, He can always fill that thirst we have for Him, and because idols are finite and below us, they will never truly fulfill us. It does not matter if they are physical idols or ungodly philosophies. Because atheists try to create their own meaning for their lives, their lives are not as fulfilled as the lives of Christians.[2]

Everything atheists pursue is finite and their human desires may eventually supersede what is available. God is far beyond anything we can create or any hobby we can partake in. This isn't to imply that our relationship with God shouldn't be close; rather, this is an acknowledgment that He is in a stratosphere far beyond us, somewhere we can never reach, and no matter how strong we become, we will always need His mercy, grace, and presence in our lives. Atheists may say that life's true joy is found in the journey of life. Indeed, there is truth in enjoying the journey, but at some point, you will have to contemplate what you are ultimately journeying toward. Is it something finite, fickle, and ephemeral? Or is it eternal, ethereal, and wholesome? The atheistic life is a small bubble of subjectivity. The best they could hope for is the freedom to live in a limited experience of their choice. The Christian, however, has opened themself up to the infinite embrace of God's majesty. No journey is without a preferred end. Atheists see the freedom of choosing one's experience to be the ultimate good. Christians see their freedom as a means to a better end, a mere steppingstone to something far greater.

C. S. Lewis opines that the fact that humans can contemplate the idea of a god is evidence that one must necessarily exist. Dogs don't have the desire to jump off trees and fly because they were not made to fly. Fish do not have the inclination to climb trees because fish do not have the necessary faculties to climb trees. Natural law dictates that when there is a desire for something, something needs to be able to satiate that desire. What separates us from animals and computers is that we have this desire for something beyond ourselves. If we were merely advanced animals, then material pleasures ought to fully satisfy us. But we aren't satisfied with that. We want something deeper. We want God.

As humans, we are able to contemplate our being and who we are in the greater universe. We can think of ourselves as something beyond our current bodies. Beyond nature itself. The idea that nature would grant us the ability to contemplate these deeper ideas, to dwell on the very possibility of external concepts, only to meditate on the nothingness and ultimate futility of it all is a sick and morbid idea. How cruel and how twisted a prospect that is.

Contemplate the worst-case scenario: What if someone decides that their life doesn't have a meaning, and they aren't interested in finding one? What if, in a moment of despair, they decide their purpose is to rebel against their very existence? Are they then granted license to kill themselves? Such a prospect is miserable, but why is it wrong? Were they not fulfilling what they believed to be their subjective life purpose? Who are we to say that they were wrong? Who are we to judge their truth?

The most meaningful pursuit of fitness first recognizes the Creator of our bodies and settles these kinds of spiritual issues.

More Important than Fitness

Even at the highest levels, there are things more important than fitness or sports. The Portland Trail Blazers point guard Damian Lillard hit a game-winning buzzer-beater against the Oklahoma City Thunder in game five of the 2019 NBA playoffs. When asked whether expectations from the previous year was creating "pressure" for him and his team, the NBA all-star said, "Pressure, nah. Fam, this is just playing ball. Pressure is the homeless man, who doesn't know where his next meal is coming from. Pressure is the single mom, who is trying to scuffle and pay her rent."[3] So yes, there are some things in life more important than fitness and sports.

While there's nothing wrong with looking fit and good, we must always remember that our body is ultimately in service to God and that obsessing about our earthly appearance is unhealthy. God wants us to give glory to Him through what He has given us. That includes our body and our fitness goals. But when fitness usurps the place of God in our lives, we must reconsider its position. If your main concern in life, your highest good, your *summum bonum*, your *raison d'être*, is fitness, sports, or anything else for that matter, then you have an idol. Fitness is meant to enhance your life, not replace it. Fitness is one piece of a larger whole, not the whole itself. In the Bible, it is made clear that God demands more zeal out of our spiritual life than anything apart from God. However important your relationship with sports or exercise is, your relationship with God should be even more important.

Fasting

Fasting is a good tool to help you keep your passions in check. Not only is it a demonstration of self-mastery, it is also an act of sacrifice. You are repeatedly saying no to your most base appetite to bring into focus your faithfulness to God. Forcefully making your life more difficult in an otherwise comfortable life can do wonders for your spiritual life. First, you develop a fiery appreciation for life. When your life becomes harder, it feels more raw. Everything starts to feel intentional. You don't feel so much that you're simply going through the motions. You also become more grateful for the life you have and for the sacrifices your ancestors made to make your life so comfortable. Second, in fasting you are saying that God is more important to you than food. Third, you are saying that it isn't only food that sustains you, but rather your steadfastness in the Lord that ultimately sustains you. Man shall not live on bread alone. Even the most nutritious meals are inadequate. You need the Word of God to sustain you. Even in your neediest moments, you are not empty because you have God. Your devotion to God is more important than your physical blessings. Fasting is the temporary foregoing of physical strength in order to bring strength to the spirit. You willingly take on trials and tribulations in order to come closer to God. Self-imposed deprivation also prepares you for the involuntary struggles of life. Since you have the practice of being deprived of things in your own controlled environment, you will be able to cope and rely on God more readily in unpredictable life events.

If you fast, you will temporarily become physically weaker, but that is not of greater concern to you than your sacrifice to God because that is what's most important. Fasting reassures you that you are more powerful with God than with the resources of this world. When you go without food, you rely on God to keep you sustained rather than relying on anything physical. Similar to David's defeating Goliath, with God, you are stronger than living by your own strength.

Perhaps unsurprisingly, fasting for short periods of time can actually be good for your physical health and athletic performance. It can help the heart function, and boost testosterone.[4] Temporary physical depletion can lead to longer-term spiritual and physical augmentation. The momentary pain is what strengthens the mind and the spirit, the recovery is what strengthens the body. For a short period of time, it is good to fast. I would recommend fasting every few months. Use sound reasoning to determine when would be the best time to do so.

Godly Vigor

So, while you can body-build and look good, or play basketball and be admired, no sport should come before God. To do so would be living for yourself. It's how we get the stereotype of big strong guys bullying weaker guys. What they care about is boosting their ego. The proper use of that strength you have is to order it towards something beyond yourself.

Part of the reason I believe there is such an overpowering societal lassitude is because there's no godly vigor. Many live for themselves and for physical pleasure. But to call this "living" would be granting it undue applause. What they experience is a bland simulacrum of life compared to the fullness of what the Christian life has to offer—a life that accepts supernatural infusion, a life that derives its purpose and identity from the Lord.

A solid and robust identity will guide how you ought to function in the world, revealing who you are and steering you toward who you ought to be. You ought to live for God, truly internalizing who He is and recognizing His will in the revelations He has given us. You don't just *understand* that God exists in the way you understand the chemical components of Saturn's rings, but you *believe* in everything He is and *actively follow* Him. To follow God isn't just to believe in Him, but to *trust* in Him. Understanding that God exists is like acknowledging a bridge exists to connect one island to another. Following God is like taking that step and actually walking across the bridge. Following

God is having faith that He will not collapse and let you fall.

You don't just extrinsically perform the rituals; you intrinsically understand that you are in a relationship with a supernatural being whose force radiates throughout every part of existence. That fact will vibrate every part of your being, permeate your very essence, penetrate your inmost core, and guide every decision you make. Everything becomes tied to this fact. Even menial tasks can have transcendent meaning when they are ultimately done for God. You are far less likely to feel a psychological malaise when you have a fire for the Lord in you, lighting up your soul and shepherding your every move. There's no question about what your role is or where you fit in the universe.

Having your identity rooted in the Lord is like having roots planted into the very core of the Earth. You are firmly placed and capable of endless growth if properly nurtured. Live infused with God, saturate yourself with His will, and bring your freedom in line with His higher values. This is not imprisonment; it's the greatest liberation, for there is nothing more freeing than the very joy of living the way you were made to live. To echo a contemporary slogan, you are able to "be your true self" in the most authentic sense. Forming your identity around your favorite sports team or video game franchise is like a twig that can easily be cut away.

Christianity isn't an evolution of your current way of living. Evolution implies the gradual change of a species through natural processes. Christianity is more of a metamorphosis, a different kind of development where a later stage becomes wholly unrecognizable to its earlier stage—as though it is a different species altogether.

To be a Christian literally means to be a little Christ. By rising from the dead, Jesus didn't only save us from sin but also bestowed on us the Holy Spirit such that we may be continually sanctified. The goal of human life is not to live for your physical strength, endurance, health, or material riches, but to align yourself with God and become like Him.

Willingness

Remember what we discussed earlier, that to be successful in life, we must cultivate the virtues of temperance and self-control. We must not willfully do things to our bodies that will result in long-term damage. For example, the Bible tells us not to be intoxicated with drugs or alcohol. If we apply that knowledge to our lives now, it will mean we should exercise temperance in all things. That instruction in the Bible tells me I have a duty to take care of my body, that not doing so would be tantamount to a bastardization of God's creation. It was true then. It is true now.

In the next chapter, we will talk about how taking care of your body and demonstrating the virtues that naturally flow from it can be beneficial to bringing people to Christ.

CHAPTER 8
The Evangelical Athlete

———————×()×———————

I am sending you out like sheep among wolves. Therefore be shrewd as snakes and as innocent as doves.
–Matthew 10:16

He who is not a good servant will not be a good master.
–Plato

If you are to be effective as good Christians you must possess strength and courage, or your example will court for little with the young, who admire strength and courage. . . . preaching does not count if it is not backed up by practice.
–Theodore Roosevelt

If you are strong in one area, chances are that you are also strong in others. Not a guarantee, but it is likely. The skills and virtues required to be excellent in one area often translate to success in other areas. On that note, being strong in one area but weak in others may put everything else about you in jeopardy. It may make you seem like a hypocrite, be viewed as someone who is shallow, or someone who feigns his success.

Stereotypically, we associate someone who is physically big with the alpha male. We think of him as a leader, successful, strong, rich, someone who gets all the women. In the same way, when a fit and muscular person defends sexual morality, people tend to take his ideas more seriously. His listeners subconsciously think, *this abstinence before marriage idea must really be something if someone like this is supporting it. If someone like him will surrender his sexual desires for something greater, there must be something to it.*

It's not only that the person being admired has rejected pleasure, but the implication is that they could capitalize on that pleasure if they so choose, yet they refuse to act on it. It is one thing to reject the desires; it's quite another to have the ability to capitalize on the desires yet purposely pass them off. (I have noticed this in my own life. People will often give my ideas more credence than they otherwise would have merely because of my big biceps.)

The Bible frequently addresses wealth and poverty, emphasizing that being rich is not inherently sinful but rather presents an opportunity to demonstrate love and generosity through God towards those in need. It is my conviction that in the same way individuals can possess material wealth, there exists a comparable form of "social wealth" that exists by developing social influence. One way to do this is through physical prowess. Applying this parallel, it follows that those who have social wealth should utilize their resources to aid the less fortunate. In short, one should leverage the influence gained through physical strength to bring people to God.

Being a man of noble character while having physical prowess is a potent combination. Perceived physical strength connotes security. You are seen as someone who is strong and reliable, yet you still put God above all of that. You recognize just how insignificant you are in comparison to God, and you believe that despite all your earthly blessings, you still desperately need Him. That kind of submission will hopefully catch people's attention, making them wonder what is so great about this God that you will bow to His authority.

Romans 12:2 says, "Do not conform any longer to the pattern of this world, but be transformed by the renewing of your mind. Then you will be able to test and approve what God's will is—his good, pleasing and perfect will." We underestimate the power of evangelization through exemplary living. Living a godly life and making that life attractive could magnetize people to your cause with powerful effectiveness.

People say that Christianity is about following a bunch of arbitrary rules that put impositions on our freedoms. But this is like saying gravity pulling us down to the earth is an imposition on our freedom. The rules of gravity are part of the nature of the universe. Likewise, the rules of Christianity are natural parts of the universe that describe the true way to live and flourish maximally. They are not arbitrary doctrines to blindly follow. When a golf coach teaches an apprentice how to swing correctly, he is not restricting his apprentice's ability to swing. Quite the opposite—he is actually teaching him how to swing. Laws, when properly placed, clarify the way to maximally flourish.

Our society is confused and broken. By living authentically Christian lives, we can be a witnesses to the true way of living. We can provide clarity and meaning, and point others to the very source of our way of life.

It's not just about being right; it's also about being effective. People will take your godly example more seriously if you take yourself more seriously. I genuinely believe, with no exaggeration, that a bunch of sprawling Muscular Christians fighting a guerrilla war against the western decline of Christianity could make profound reverberations in the culture.

This is why I think that physical fitness can ultimately help in the effective spreading of the gospel. There's something authoritative about a muscular person making claims that attracts attention to himself. His physique connotes confidence and sternness. It makes him someone who commands respect. The unconscious message is that he has mastered his own body; therefore, he is someone who knows how to get things done. So we can follow his advice.

This is not to say that if you are not fit you cannot preach the gospel. Far from it. God uses people of all shapes and colors to reach the heart of men and women. He even uses nature and animals and children to reach the world. My statement above is from my under-standing of the psychology of how human beings subconsciously think. I merely offer an under-utilized route to evangelization that we should explore.

Throughout the history of advertising, people have used "experts" to gain trust from the population. This is why medical videos have al-ways used doctors (or people pretending to be doctors) to advertise their products. It shows a level of trust when someone looks as if they know what they are talking about, especially in a field we may not be familiar with. Likewise, fitness advertisements often use extremely muscular individuals to advertise their products because they represent someone who looks like our definition of fitness.

We learn from psychology that world leaders who exhibit more masculine qualities are more respected in governments. This is why fe-male political leaders try to look more androgynous.[1] Aspects resem-bling masculinity tend to elicit primal authority. In primal and tradi-tional societies men are typically the head of the family and the ones who acquire and take charge of most of the resources—or at least they're expected to. Their deep voices, their larger statures, and their greater physical strength when compared to their female counterparts become synonymous with their being the central authoritative figures in their wives' and their children's lives. In modern societies this same pattern tends to arise in subcultures and in leadership spheres. Thus, it is no wonder female politicians attempt to emulate them.

Politicians who are successful in other areas of life, like business, are also more highly respected. The implicit belief is that since they have their own life figured out and are successful in one field, they are capable of leading people to success in other areas. To remix an adage from Jordan Peterson, they have set their own house in order and have therefore earned the right to criticize the world. As an example, whether you love or hate Donald Trump this is partly what gave him a leg up when he was running for the US presidency in 2016. His followers were impressed by his reputation as a successful businessman, as someone who goes after what he wants and is successful at doing so. Similarly, being in good shape confirms to your audience that you have put your *fitness* house in order.

A study by Sandra Praxmarer at the University of Augsburg, Germany, showed that attractive people are more persuasive than unattractive people in the world of advertisement and product sales.[2] A Cornell University study found that those who were more attractive faced on average twenty-two months less time in prison.[3] If being in better physical shape makes you more attractive, that would imply that physical fitness makes you more persuasive and likable. One could extend this to matters of philosophy, politics, and religion.

On my YouTube channel DrUpauli, I have a video titled, "What is the Point of Living?"[4] In it I talk about big issues such as depression, love, and finding purpose. Throughout that video, I had clips of me working out interspersed with stock images of what I was talking about, and clips from the anime *Welcome to the NHK* because I use that show to illustrate my ideas. The feedback I have received from that video was that it helped a lot of people. But one person's feedback especially stood out to me. Instead of leaving a public comment, this viewer sent me a direct message. I will not give out his name for the sake of privacy, but he told me that I could share his message. Here is what he said:

> I think the points you made and the overall message of the
> video w[ere] very strong. For someone who is struggling in

life and doesn't understand their misery, this was probably one of the best resources to improve my life. I will definitely recommend it to people I meet. I especially liked [it] when you talked about sacrifice and the necessity of it, and how it can actually benefit your life.

There is something very striking about your oratory style, and I genuinely believe it helped me focus during the video, but even outside of that, the things you were saying were intuitive yet incredibly insightful; it's the type of video that makes you think "Dang, I've had that inkling of a thought before, but I never knew quite how to articulate it," and that's the best type of video, honestly.

I also liked how you incorporated your beliefs into the video without being [too] pushy. I think this is probably part of your oratory style as well; you [speak] authoritatively and assertively, but in a comforting manner so that people can process it, which is rare.

It was nice that you didn't "hold back." In a sense, within the first minute or so I knew exactly what kind of person you were because you didn't hide what you meant, very straight to the point, but in a way that implicitly desired to help those in need. I enjoyed the philosophical tones of the whole thing. I think my favorite part was at the end where you said that happiness doesn't mean avoiding suffering, but rather, embracing it, and becoming stronger because of it. I'm paraphrasing there, but you know what I mean. That was very powerful, and I hadn't considered it before. . . .

Also, is that you working out in the video? If it is, you are in great shape, and it definitely gives you credentials as far as improving oneself is concerned.

What's important to note is how he described my oratory style. He said it was authoritative and direct but welcoming enough not to turn people off. I was hitting my audience with my honest opinions but in a way that was respectful and kind so that they could digest my opinions even if they were of a dissenting view. It also helped that they could see that I was muscular. This meant that a lot of what I talk about in that video, I actually practice. Muscularity is the most visual manifestation of self-improvement. Thus, it gave me "credentials" without actually having formal credentials to my name at the time. A lot of what I said wouldn't have the same punch if I didn't demonstrate the virtue myself.

This is the kind of balance I believe Jesus was able to ride. When talking to people, He spoke in a convincing and honest way but was still open and welcoming. Jesus lived a perfect life, so we know that He practiced what He preached.

With the power imputed to you through your new looks from exercise comes the personal responsibility to live a disciplined life. That is exactly what athletics teaches you. Athletes are regimented and disciplined. Athletes must be cognizant of their diet, the time they train, and be very meticulous in the way that they practice. Consider the sport (or art, depending on who you ask) of bodybuilding. Bodybuilding requires eating healthy and working out consistently. For dedicated bodybuilders, this would mean counting your calories, timing your meals, and timing your workouts. It is a 24/7 lifestyle.

This kind of discipline is analogous to our walk as Christians. Being a Christian isn't just going to church every Sunday, it is a lifestyle you live every day. Bodybuilding requires resisting the temptations of fatty foods; Christianity requires resisting vices like pride and lust. Bodybuilding tells you that you shouldn't always listen to the desires of your body because you are working towards a higher goal. It teaches you delayed gratification. If you don't eat donuts now, your body will thank you later. Christianity similarly teaches you self-control (a.k.a. temperance). You may find it difficult to think, *if I don't sin now, my soul will thank me later.* But that's the truth.

In the next chapter, we will discuss in greater detail how physical discipline can manifest itself into spiritual discipline, but before we conclude this chapter, I will leave you with this some words from Theodore Roosevelt:

> If we read the Bible aright, we read a book which teaches us to go forth and do the work of the Lord; to do the work of the Lord in the world as we find it; to try to make things better in this world, even if only a little better, because we have lived in it. That kind of work can be done only by the man who is neither a weakling nor a coward; by the man who in the fullest sense of the word is a true Christian.[5]

CHAPTER 9
Physical and Mental Fortitude

———————————×< >×————————————

Do not be overcome by evil, but overcome evil with good.
—Romans 12:21

He who is only an athlete is too crude, too vulgar, too much a savage.
He who is a scholar only is too soft, too effeminate. The ideal citizen is the scholar
athlete, the man of thought and the man of action.
—Plato

I count him braver who overcomes his desires than him who conquers his enemies,
for the hardest victory is over self.
—Aristotle

Civilize the mind, but make savage the body.
—Ancient Chinese Proverb

Difficulties strengthen the mind, as labor does the body.
—Seneca

Hardships often prepare ordinary people for an extraordinary destiny.
—C. S. Lewis

As we have seen in earlier chapters, physical discipline can manifest itself in spiritual discipline. Virtues do not exist in a vacuum. The virtues you get from physical fitness can be applied to your everyday life, including your spiritual life. Virtues such as discipline, self-care, and sacrifice are very precious. The apostle Paul even compares believers to "athletes" who must "train" their souls and run the race of life that has been set for them. 1 Corinthians 9:27 (NLT) speaks to this point. It says, "I discipline my body like an athlete, training it to do what it should. Otherwise, I fear that after preaching to others I myself might be disqualified."

Playing sports can be very humbling. When you play, you run the risk of being outmatched, physically humbled, or shown that sometimes you just have to take it on the chin. If you have ever played competitive sports, you are familiar with all these experiences. Athletes understand these lessons. There is something about being physically humbled that really gets to you.

Likewise, every Christian must metaphorically take hits to the chin. The Bible recognizes this and teaches believers to equip themselves with "the armor of God."

This includes the *belt of truth*, which holds the armor together, similar to how the truth must surround us and hold our life together. There is the *shield of faith* to defend us. Our faith is our first line of defense; it's the mindset and commitment by which we live.

We are also equipped with the *breastplate of righteousness*, which guards us against all the evil that surrounds us. The physical breastplate protects the vital organs like the heart, lungs, and liver; the spiritual breastplate protects your core from every spiritual attack. Perhaps this implies that when our faith (our shield) is overwhelmed or we are blind-sighted, we rely on our righteousness—the intrinsic character traits we have built through discipline.

Another part of our armor is the *sword of the Spirit*. The sword, identified as the Word of God, is for battling the evil forces that come our way. It is the only accessory in the Christian armory that allows you to attack. We have no way of fighting the enemy unless we have God's Word and Spirit within us. It means that we should work in alignment with Scripture and by the leading of the Holy Spirit to fight and ultimately conquer the evil in our lives.

The next piece of armor is the *helmet of salvation*. Knowing who we are as saved, redeemed, people—our identity in Christ—is critical to any victory. The helmet is the mark of God, a bloodied doorway to our soul which signifies our allegiance to the Kingdom of God. Living out the life made possible by Jesus' sacrifice on the cross is fundamental to our fight.

The last piece of armor, the *feet fitted with the readiness of the gospel of peace* relates to the shoes worn by Roman soldiers of the day. They were lightweight and sturdy, useable in any situation at a moment's notice. Every step we take is gospel-inspired, and we must always be ready to act.

When we are staying holy and pure with the gospel, we can stand firm and confident against the enemy.

In the battle of life, you will be overwhelmed. That is how relentlessly the enemy of your soul will fight you. The world may hate you because you dare to be different. But you must persevere and, as many times as you fall, you must get up and go back into the battlefield. This is analogous to getting in shape and staying fit. It requires discipline and obstinate determination to stay on course and get to the finish line. You will be tempted many times to give up and relax, but like the Christian equipped with the armor of God, you must pull out one aspect of the arsenal after another to fight and fight and fight again. And with the divine might from the Lord empowering your every move, you will seize victory over the enemy with overwhelming godly gusto.

Working out at the gym teaches you how to be self-sufficient, confident, and to understand things like slow, earned progression. This teaches you personal responsibility. Once you go to the gym and start losing weight or gaining muscle all on your own, you realize that other problems you may be having could also be solved if you work at them and don't give up. You begin to realize that there is power within you to change your life. We have all envisioned that ideal, greatest version of ourselves. The grand vision of our loftiest aspirations. It's not as though there is some labyrinthine matrix stopping you, you have the power to materialize him—you simply choose not to. People who blame all their problems on "the system" are never happy or content. When you blame abstract concepts for all your shortcomings, how are you supposed to get better? People who spend time working on themselves understand the importance of self-reliance. They develop a desire to take responsibility for their actions and their outcomes.

Physical strength also gives you an appreciation for strength because you know what it takes to get there. Since you have used weights and have been progressively overloading, you understand how to control the weights of life better. When you know what it takes to acquire strength, you respect it more.

Everyone has a cross that they must bear. But being human, the grass always seems greener on the other side of the fence. Thus, few believe their cross is the one they deserve. They look around, compare themselves to other people, and conclude that the cross others bear is less burdensome than their own. Yet this is precisely the point. Each cross borne is uniquely designed to bring out your best self. It weeds out your weaknesses and makes you the best you that you can be—for God's glory. The cross you bear is the most difficult for you precisely because you are the one who has the most to gain from it. God has already given you the tools you need to be as effective as you can. It's your job to use them, to do the best you can with them, to sharpen them, to keep them oiled and ready for battle, and to kill the parts hurting your ability to do that.

With that said, it is important to couple your mental discipline with mental acuity. In *Spark: The Revolutionary New Science of Exercise and the Brain*, John J. Ratey speaks of man's ability to digest new information by exercising. This is thanks to dopamine and the production of the protein BDNF (brain-derived neurotrophic factor).[1] Staying in shape is a great way to keep yourself not only physically but also mentally sharp. The stress from exercise promotes protein production in the brain and helps the formation of new cells, which primes your brain to learn new things. BDNF is the most important protein that gets boosted as it propels the growth of new neurons. Exercise improves the connections between neurons by allowing them to become more efficient.

The effect exercise has on our ability to digest information has been shown empirically as well. Kids with higher fitness scores have routinely scored higher in academics than kids with lower fitness scores (as seen in the research by the California department of education.)[2]

There is also some evidence to suggest a link between moderate exercise and higher IQ scores.[3] This only goes to further prove the connection between the mind, body, and spirit. I have talked about influencing people a lot, but of course, you still have to be intelligent and articulate. Otherwise, you risk coming off like a babbling Neanderthal—all brawn and no brain. Articulate what you believe and why you believe it with cogency, veracity, and grace.

First Peter 3:15 says, "Always be prepared to give an answer to everyone who asks you to give the reason for the hope that you have. But do this with gentleness and respect." Thus, you must know what you believe, why you believe it, and be prepared to defend it. This is the type of mindset that exercise can help foster.

Facing Temptations with Wisdom

A disciplined athlete is resolute in his commitment. Consider how Jesus withstood the devil's temptation to veer Him off the course of His earthly mission. Jesus quoted from the Bible. The devil tried to misuse a Bible verse, taking it out of context and using it against Jesus. But Jesus understood the theology holistically and called the devil out on all the temptations. How often do people in society misquote Bible verses? How often do we encounter situations where we try to justify things we know are wrong but still go through with anyway? How often do we have compulsions that society tells us are okay and harmless based on some loose interpretation of the issue? These are all the same flimsy rationales meant to entice us to do the wrong thing. As Jesus did, we must resist temptations by using a studious understanding of God's Word to help us.

Consider again the conversation between the serpent and Eve in the Garden of Eden. The serpent told Eve, "Did God really say, 'You must not eat from any tree in the garden'?" (Genesis 3:1). When Eve saw that the fruit was pleasing to the eye and could make her wise, she gave in. But in seeking to be wise, she became foolish. That is the issue with temptation: It promises what it cannot provide and leaves us unfulfilled and regretful when it has run its course in our lives. It looks superficially pleasing to the eye but is never good in the long run.

We live in a culture full of temptations, perhaps on a scale never seen before. We face temptations to do things that superficially appear pleasing but ultimately lead to death. Take, for example, the temptation to eat unhealthily. Unlike in past eras, there is now an abundance of all types of food. Much of our food is concocted in laboratories, highly processed by machines, and full of unhealthy additives, with lots of sodium and sugar (or carcinogenic sugar substitutes). You may think that the temptation to eat unhealthy food may not rank high on the scale of big temptations, but it is a huge problem for many people. Not giving in to the urge is certainly a good training ground for more serious issues. Will power works like a muscle in that it can be developed as such by giving it lighter weights to train with.

Referring to Plato's quote at the beginning of the chapter, we should strive to be "scholarly athletes." (Similar terms are "Warrior Poet," "Educated Barbarian," and "Philosopher Thug," though I prefer "scholarly athlete.") We must strive to be both physically and mentally strong. The mind and body are God's gift to us, and we ought to make the most of them. When you successfully combine your physical and mental attributes, you will become dangerous. Not because people will fear for their lives when they see you, but because you will be effective in whatever you set your mind on.

British Army officer William Butler said, "The nation that will insist on drawing a broad line of demarcation between the fighting man and the thinking man is liable to find its fighting done by fools and its thinking done by cowards."[4] Consider that for a while. Between the body and the mind is a synergistic link that both thrives on and benefits both. Be well-rounded. You must hone both the mind and body to maximize your effectiveness in both realms.

One who spends all his time reading and educating has no practical experience. He might begin to regard regular interactions with people as something odd because he is not used to it. Some psychologists reduce the human experience to a collection of twitches, muscle movements, and reactions. Such is partially the case, but in the final analysis, this only reveals a rudimentary understanding of humans. Such an attempt at anthropology could barely pass for explaining the makeup of an animal.

A scholarly athlete is one who understands the broader human nature, and one who understands specific human interactions. He sees both the forest for the trees and the trees for the forest. He understands the broad philosophical nature of mankind as well as its specific differences and idiosyncrasies. He has good psychology substantiated by proper philosophical axioms.

After cultivating strength through exercise, it's important to remain humble—not only in fitness, but also in the manner in which you conduct yourself in the presence of God. Ensure that you are not only mentally alert to God, but when possible and appropriate, make an attempt to be physically present. For example, when you pray, don't just think the prayers in your head while lying on your bed or sitting in front of the television. Instead, get on your knees, close your eyes for concentration, fold and raise your hands in supplication, open your mouth, and talk to your God. This shows some seriousness in the exercise of prayer. It is not a performance of piety. It is a posture of humility before your Creator.

Brain and Brawn Together

Leonardo Da Vinci is best known for his intellect and art, but there are many accounts of him being physically fit as well. Factfiend.com says,

> According to most every historical account of da Vinci ever written, the Renaissance painter was stunningly handsome and possessed a lean, muscular figure well into his old age. . . . Along with being able to effortlessly bend iron horseshoes, in his youth Leonardo could grasp iron door knockers in his large, man-sized hands and crush them with little to no apparent exertion on his part and was known to earn extra money by challenging local tough guys to see who could throw a large rock the farthest.[5]

Many people believe that playing brain training games or something similar can preserve long-term brain health. This may be partly true, but by far the most effective training for extended brain health brain is physical exercise. Neurological research has proved that fifty-two hours of exercise improved cognitive performance among older adults (aged sixty and above) regardless of whether they had previous cognitive impairments or not.[6]

In the next chapter, we will discuss the impact of exercise on professional Christian athletes. But to conclude this chapter, consider some words from former US President John F. Kennedy:

> The physical fitness of our citizens is a vital prerequisite to America's realization of its full potential as a nation, and to the opportunity of each individual citizen to make full and fruitful use of his capacities.

> Physical fitness is not only one of the most important keys to a healthy body, it is the basis of dynamic and creative intellectual activity. The relationship between the soundness of the body and the activities of the mind is subtle and complex. Much is not yet understood. But we do know what the Greeks knew: that intelligence and skill can only function at the peak of their capacity when the body is healthy and strong.[7]

CHAPTER 10
Christianity and Athletes

———————————✕ ✕———————————

Make every effort to supplement your faith with virtue, and virtue with knowledge,
and knowledge with self-control, and self-control with steadfastness,
and steadfastness with godliness,
–2 Peter 1:5–6 (ESV)

What good will it be for someone to gain the whole world,
yet forfeit their soul?
–Matthew 16:26

L et us start here by debunking the idea that Christians should never publicly announce their faith. People read Matthew 6:5, "And when you pray, do not be like the hypocrites, for they love to pray standing in the synagogues and on the street corners to be seen by others," and make it sound as if God doesn't want you to ever make your faith public. That is obviously not true. Throughout the Bible are many verses espousing the exact opposite of that sentiment. This verse refers to those who display their worship so that others can praise them for their apparent piety.

Some people dislike it when athletes publicly give thanks to God for their athletic performance. They resent it because they think the athletes are saying God literally did all the work for them and that they didn't do anything through their own efforts. Such critics argue that attributing a great feat to God detracts from the work the athletes themselves put into their achievements. (As if anyone has anything God has not given them the strength and ability to do!)

But I don't think that's what athletes entirely mean when they thank God for their successes. They are thanking God for the opportunity He has provided, for the people He provided to help them get there, for their God-given abilities, and for the good health to perform. They are thanking God for giving them the will to push forward. If God had not provided the ability and the resources, they would not have reached that stage in their careers.

Deliberate Choice Required

If you were to ask someone who is overweight and out of shape how they came to their physical condition, they would probably give you a mix of accident, bewilderment, or tell you that it is a product of their genetics. If you ask someone who is in shape how they came into their physical condition, they would likely give you a five-step plan with twelve rules to follow. Vice happens by accident or inattention. Virtue requires deliberate choice. We must constantly look to God and make deliberate attempts to maintain our spiritual shape. When you ignore your physical and spiritual health, you become susceptible to disease, obesity, vice, and sin.

It is hard for some Christian athletes to stay loyal to God while focusing on their sport, especially in the major leagues. They must grapple with the external pressures of being a celebrity, being rich, and relating to non-believing teammates. Even amateur level athletes face similar pressures, though not at such an intense level. Over the years, successful athletes would acquire fame, status, money, and power, all of which will tempt them to fall into spiritual decline. The Bible says that "it is easier for a camel to go through the eye of a needle than for a rich man to get into heaven" for good reason. The combination of influence and affluence, if bereft the presence of perfected virtue, fans the flames of our sinful inclinations.

The spiritual decline is a gradual descent. You start to think you do not need God in your life, that you can do anything and everything by your own power and strength. Before long, God's blessings mean less and less, and you start to take His mercies for granted. Maintaining religious devotion soon becomes arduous and painful. When you reject God once, it can set into motion a cascade that creates negative spiritual inertia. Perhaps you begin to prioritize pot and prostitutes over prayer and penance. The decline is not rapid or sudden; it's a slow downfall. It's like an undetectable poison that gradually eats you up. You don't exactly know what date it was that kicked it off, but you eventually realize you are corroding, and that your spiritual death is imminent if the trend continues.

Most athletes are not prepared for the immediate wealth that comes to them. From relative obscurity, many are suddenly endowed with fame and fortune. Of course, they have worked diligently to get where they are; athletic ability cannot be feigned or denied. But when they reach that point, the turnaround from grass to grace happens swiftly, and many of them don't know how to handle it.

To put this in the big picture, I think this is partly why Christianity is declining in our modern world. We are now so self-sufficient that we cease to revere our Maker. God no longer matters to us; other things are more important, and we begin to worship those things instead of God. This could be our ego, our wealth, our looks, or our pleasures. As Nietzsche described it, when God is dead, something else will have to take His place. Everyone is a slave to something. It's unavoidable. Will you be a slave to your earthly passions or transcend that and become a slave to righteousness? (Romans 6:16). Earthly passions ought not be everything. They do not satisfy the longings of the human heart. What happens if the fame, money, athleticism, and skills leave? They are not transcendent to who you are. They are fleeting. If the money, fame, and skill were to go tomorrow, then who are you?

Back to our pro athletes, a lot of them are in spiritual comas. Of course, since many of them come from poor circumstances, they could have ended up on the street selling drugs, stealing, and eventually ending up in prison. Sports saved them and gave them a purpose for living. Sports help young people, but it doesn't fix all their problems. It certainly does not fix their innermost problems. This is where their devotion to Jesus Christ comes in.

Lifestyle

As we have established so far, many athletes come from humble backgrounds, so they know what it is like to really work for something. They have likely dealt with fatherlessness, drugs, and street living, and don't want to go back to that life. Thus they must stay disciplined and stand strong in faith if they want substantial healing.

The reality, however, is that most of these athletes would rather spend their newfound fortune ostentatiously on fancy cars, expensive houses, and the latest yachts. There is no dispute that the money is theirs to spend as they like. Some point to the jobs their lavish lifestyle creates for others, like drivers, housekeepers, cooks, tailors, and hairdressers—and argue that this is not a bad thing after all. However, it is clear that such a lifestyle does not align with a Christian focus. Christian pro athletes should meaningfully and intentionally influence society for the glory of God.

The lifestyle of celebrities and people in higher social circles often result in social degeneracy. Many pro athletes have earned a reputation of being violent and abusive in their domestic lives. The reasons for this can sometimes include drug usage and sports-induced injuries.

"Roid rage" is a term used to describe those who become more aggressive due to supraphysiological testosterone consumption. These athletes already produce a lot of natural testosterone, so when some of them supercharge their hormones, they create adverse consequences.

Another reason for their violent reputation is chronic brain injury that many athletes suffer, especially those in high-contact sports. Chronic Traumatic Encephalopathy (CTE) is a neurodegenerative disease that occurs after years of constant blows to the head, common in high-contact sports, which can lead to behavioral problems.[1] I am not saying that these athletes are to be morally exempt from the consequences of their misbehaviors and crimes. I'm saying that their wealth, their fame, and even their neurology are factors that can feed into the culture that can lead them down the path of spiritual decline.

Pro athletes are also known for their sexual degeneracy. NBA Hall of Famer Wilt Chamberlain famously claimed that he had slept with 20,000 women.[2] I don't believe I need to point out how out of line this is with Christian teachings. This is why we are all pleasantly surprised and impressed when we hear of pro athletes that retire to become pastors and community leaders. We can only imagine the difficulties in their lifestyles they had to overcome in order to hold their heads above water and emerge still holding on to their faith. These people are full of such spiritual engagement that they are able to hold on to their faith despite the temptations of the world. They have their faith and their athletics working in symbiosis. They are Muscular Christians.

Exemplary Athletes

It is appropriate at this juncture to highlight some exemplary Christian athletes of our time. These are people whose faith was undeterred by the corrosion of their society. These athletes have become the motivation for younger Christian athletes still trying to make it as professionals in their various sports. Of course, the following is not an exhaustive list of Christian pro athletes, just some of those who have been vocal about their faith and its influence in their lives.

Kevin Fast is a Lutheran Canadian pastor who is one of the

strongest men in the world. In an interview with the New York Post, he mentions some of his Guinness World Records and feats: To name a few, he has pulled fifteen cars at once; he has pulled a train, a plane, a house, arm wrestled a fire truck, and lifted twenty-two people on his back.[3]

Tim Tebow was one of the best American College Football players during his time at the University of Florida. He was raised by Baptist parents and often prays during football games. There's a term dubbed "Tebowing" in acknowledgment of this. Tebow has shared his Christian faith in schools, churches, youth groups, and even prisons.[4,5] Tebow practices Christian sexual ethics, and claims that he maintained his virginity until he was married.[6,7]

The former Chicago White Stockings (now called White Sox) baseball player Billy Sunday attracted large groups of people to his sermons. Billy preached an uber-macho, testosterone-soaked Christianity. His Muscular credentials and no-nonsense approach to Christianity attracted many men to the Christian fold.[8]

Some other athletes include Jaelene Hinkle, a female soccer player who has been public about her Christian beliefs, and Jerone Davidson, an ex-NFL player and current pastor.

All of these athletes overcame temptations to compromise their faith when they were professional athletes. They acknowledge that their successes were not because of their power, but by the Spirit of the Lord working with, in, and through them.

CHAPTER 11

The Virtues of Athletics

*A well-built physique is more than vanity. It shows discipline,
dignity, and dedication. It requires patience, passion, and self-respect.
It cannot be bought, stolen, or inherited.
It cannot be held onto without constant work.*

—Arnold Schwarzenegger

*A well-built physique is a status symbol. It reflects you worked hard for it, no
money can buy it. You cannot inherit it. You cannot steal it. You cannot borrow it.
You cannot hold on to it without constant work. It shows dedication.
It shows discipline. It shows self-respect. It shows dignity. It shows patience, work
ethic, and passion. That is why it's attractive to me.*

—Pauline Nordin

*The aim of art is to represent not the outward appearance of things,
but their inward significance.*

—Aristotle

A thletics is a microcosm of social Christian faith in at least three areas. In team sports, you must learn how to be both a follower and a leader; in individual sports, you must learn how to work with a coach or mentor; in bodybuilding, you must be disciplined at all hours of the day and learn to compare yourself to yourself and to appreciate individual, tangible progress.

Team Sports

It's important to be strong on your own, but it is also important to work with other people. Team sports teaches you the value of teamwork. Team sports require every player to have a role. In soccer we have the goalie, defense, midfielders, and strikers. In basketball we have the guards, forwards, and centers. In football we have the quarterback, linebacker, cornerback, wide receiver, and many more.

Each player is specially gifted and properly trained to fulfill their own role. It's important to understand where you are needed and what you are needed for—and to fulfill the duties assigned to you.

In *The Way of Men*, Jack Donovan describes the tactical values of a man as strength, courage, mastery, and honor. In his hypothetical band of gang members, these were the traits most desired and respected. In his section on mastery, he talks about a man's ability to cultivate and demonstrate proficiency at a given task. This is the ability to become not dependent, not independent, but interdependent. In Donavan's band, dependency means you are powerless. Independence means you are alone, and when you are alone, you are vulnerable. Independence makes the unit less efficient because everyone feels that they have to do everything by themselves, unable to get help from others.[1] Ecclesiastes 4:9–12 speaks of the values of interdependence:

> Two are better than one, because they have a good return
> for their labor: If either of them falls down, one can help the
> other up. But pity anyone who falls and has no one to help
> them up. Also, if two lie down together, they will keep
> warm. But how can one keep warm alone? Though one may
> be overpowered, two can defend themselves. A cord of three
> strands is not quickly broken.

Nobody wants to be lonely and vulnerable. For the band to be efficient, the band members must be interdependent. This means that everyone will work together while focusing on their strengths and continually relying on each other for success while building a sense of comradery amongst each other.

Think about what happens in basketball when someone tries to play hero ball. They take every shot, never pass the ball, and try to win the game by themselves. But even Michael Jordan, arguably the most clutch player in the history of that sport, would sometimes defer to his teammates for the final shot. This is what he did in game six of the 1997 NBA Finals when he passed to Steve Kerr to make the game-winning shot against the Utah Jazz. Being interdependent means being reliable and working within your tribe. It means to understand your role and understand that you provide something unique to the team. Being interdependent occupies that sweet spot where you can work with other people and also work on your own.

It is important to understand where you specialize and maximize your effectiveness there. The Bible speaks of how everyone has their own gifts, which they must utilize for work in the body of Christ. Some people have the gift of wisdom, some have the gift of healing, some have the gift of evangelism (1 Corinthians 12 and Romans 12). Everyone has a role to play. If one team member doesn't play their role, the group will not be maximally successful. When everyone is working together, the benefits go beyond an additional effect and transform into a multiplying effect due to how everyone is uniquely taking advantage of their strengths. This creates a division of labor with each job depending on the other. Just as in team sports, everyone is needed to build the kingdom of God.

First Corinthians 12:12–26 speaks of how we are all different body parts of the body of Christ. Some of us are hands, some are feet, some are eyes. The body can only function if we all play our roles. Certain people have certain gifts best fit for specific roles. We aren't all supposed to be doing the same thing. A body can't move if it only has brains, and the body can't think if it only has muscles. Similar to volleyball, we need setters and spikers. The spikers get all the attention, but they are wholly ineffective without the setters by their side. Similarly, in Christianity, some roles get more attention than others, but they are all important and depend on one another. To win in team sports requires the team to be in constant self-denial and practice dutiful self-effacement. It calls on everyone to work as a team for the good of the team. In Christianity, we are similarly called to be humble and realize that we are not the main thing. There is a transcendent cause divinely above us. We are merely one part of the kingdom-building process. So don't get ahead of yourself, know your place, and do your job.

That doesn't mean however that you cannot perform outside of your gift. Some people are more attuned to one gift over the other, but I don't think that Paul meant for us to be rigid. We should still be adequate in other functions. Suppose someone asks you for help at a time they are hurting. Would you say to them, "Well, you're out of luck, dude. My gift is evangelism, not healing." Compare this again to volleyball. In volleyball, with every new possession, the server changes. This means that everyone ought to be an adequate server. Everyone must know how to get the ball rolling, figuratively and literally speaking. This is the same in the social Christian sphere. Believers should be able to exercise multiple gifts to bring glory to God. They must know enough to get the ball rolling, even if it doesn't lie perfectly within their specialty.

Getting better at side roles may even help you get better in your main role. This is because you gain a more holistic understanding of the world. As I have explained in previous chapters, the functions of your body, mind, and soul are all interconnected. So too are evangelism, healing, and wisdom.

In summary, everyone should be a jack of all trades and master of some. You don't need to be a pro athlete, but having adequate cardiovascular endurance is a good thing. You don't need a Ph.D. in theology, but you should understand the Word well.

In team sports, you must also readily help your teammates. That is a necessity in order to play effectively and to get the best results. Of course, it helps if you are comrades and have a mutual appreciation for each other and bond together not only in the sport but outside of it as well.

The same is true of our faith. You will often help your brothers and sisters in faith, and by doing so, you will grow in comradery with your fellow believers.

Individual Sports

The story of Job is the quintessential example of suffering and of trusting God through it. The book of Job is about God and Satan having a celestial bet on whether Job will sin and curse God if given enough suffering. Satan believes that Job's faith is superficial and susceptible to corruption, given disastrous circumstances, but God knows it is not so. Therefore, God allows Satan to test Job's faith, stripping him of his family, wealth, and health. In this season, Job must suffer in isolation and overcome the unfair trials and temptations of the enemy. At the end of the book, God finally responds to Job through a whirlwind and asks him a series of questions that highlight His power, wisdom, and sovereignty over creation. After this, Job responds by trusting in God's wisdom, realizes his limited understanding, and acknowledges God's supreme authority.

Your strength as a team is important, but so also is your strength and confidence as an individual. Individual sports teach you how to work by yourself, and with a coach. They teach you how to deal with pain and how to persist through odds and cultivate individual strength. Perseverance is a Christian virtue that is of integral importance to persist through the struggles of life. There are moments in Christianity that you must push through pain without help from other believers. This is a necessary step towards making the faith your own. Similarly, your progression in individual sports is an endeavor where your progress is largely determined by your own will.

On July 11, 1996, Andrew Golota, a heavyweight contender, fought Riddick Bowe, a former heavyweight champion. Golota was an impressive boxer who showcased incredible boxing skills, which helped him dominate the early rounds. However, as the fight progressed, Golota's endurance began to wane. In the seventh round Golota's fatigue and frustration boiled over, leading to a series of unscrupulous behavior. He repeatedly struck Bowe below the belt, resulting in multiple fouls and point deductions. After the fourth low blow in the seventh round, the referee had no choice but to disqualify Golota. The grueling pace of the match had taken a toll on him, and he fell into an incandescent seethe. He was on the verge of exploding with rage, he tried his hardest to contain it, but it still leaked. Just as Golota's frustration mounted when Bowe refused to yield, Satan's efforts against Job reach a breaking point. Faced with Job's unwavering endurance and steadfast faith, Satan realizes the futility of his attacks. Like a sore loser throwing a temper tantrum, he starts using morally corrupt tactics. First, he attacks Job's wealth, then goes for his family and personal health. All in a futile attempt to catch him off guard, but with God on Job's side, Satan fails.

In individual sports, you cannot rely on your team to bail you out when you have a bad day. Similarly, in Christianity, you are in ultimate control of your faith. You must choose it yourself. Your friends and mentors can help you and guide you, but it ultimately comes down to you and your own will. Will you trust in God no matter what? Can you trust Him to help you endure the trials of life? Is your faith strong, or will your crumble in weakness as troubling situations occur? Do you depend on God to arm you with unyielding perseverance, or will you succumb to the weight of Satan? Satan hits Job with a relentless flurry of physical, spiritual, and mental attacks. He hits Job in the vital organs and even used some flagrant maneuvers to inflict more harm on Job. Job endures a living hell with no one to console him. His only option is to put his trust in the Lord.

The problem of suffering is probably the biggest philosophical objection to Christianity. But paradoxically, it is only through a powerful faith in the Lord that you have the right philosophical framework to push through suffering. If life has no meaning, there is no divine purpose, moral framework, or hope in the future that might animate you to persist through the suffering of life. But if life does have meaning, then suffering is giving you a chance to come closer to God, a chance to make you stronger and refine your character.

The realm of running provides an apt metaphor for the spiritual endurance of pain. A marathon is a grueling test of endurance. As athletes lace their shoes and embark on long-distance races, they willingly subject themselves to physical and mental pain and exhaustion. In the crucible of suffering, they shed their weakness and discover their hidden reservoirs of strength, unleashing the dormant force within. It is through this restless pursuit that they transcend their physical and mental limitations to attain a level of greatness reserved only for the few who are willing to endure. Each step taken in agony becomes a testament to the indomitable human spirit. Similarly, in life, it is through suffering that victory is snatched from the jaws of defeat, and triumph is claimed over the force of the devil.

The marathon is the culmination of all their efforts as they finally reach that ethereal finish line. The finish line crowns their valiant journey and is a symbol of personal triumph. When the athlete finishes, he is panting and staggering under the weight of his limbs. When he completes the race, he lies down gasping in bliss as the suffering has temporarily ended. Comparably, in Christianity, we have future hope in the *eternal* victory over suffering. Life is a marathon race where heaven is the sweet delight waiting for us in the end.

Each second you shave off your mile time is a battle won. Everything you did that you did not want to do in pursuit of running the race has strengthened your will, preparing it for the big test of the competition. And in the race of life, as you build a habit of prayer and thanksgiving, you are similarly preparing your spiritual will for the disastrous predicaments that may befall your life. You will win as Job won because you have God by your side. And with God by your side, no weapon formed against you will prosper.

Bodybuilding

Bodybuilding is the most physical manifestation of personal development. The tangible results you acquire in bodybuilding set it apart from all other forms of self-improvement. It is the most visual form of self-improvement.

The aim of bodybuilding is to become a better version of yourself, to patiently climb the ladder of personal progress. The competition is you. You strive for perfection in every little detail. It is not mindless weightlifting. You calculate everything. You must time your rest and check your food more so than in any other sport. You are working on your body to become the best version of yourself.

In the book *Everything Bad is Good for You: How Today's Popular Culture Is Actually Making Us Smarter* by Steven Johnson, he talks about how video games of the early 2000s are extremely effortful and only provide gratification after hard work. He says, "You'll often hear video games included on the list of the debased instant gratifications that abound in our culture, right up there with raunchy music videos and fast food. But compared to most forms of popular entertainment, games turn out to be all about delayed gratification."[2]

Bodybuilding is much the same. Seeing the progress you make after months of hitting the gym taps into that same satisfying feeling you get from slowly leveling up in a video game. Unlike in many other things where your efforts aren't always rewarded, in gaming and bodybuilding you are always guaranteed results, often directly proportional to the amount of work you put in. There is nothing more meritocratic. The results of your efforts are concomitant to the work you put in to get there. These are results you will be satisfied with for a long time. Bodybuilding and video games feed into that innate desire we have to work, to improve, and to one day feel gratified for our work. In video games, the results are contained within the game. But in bodybuilding your results actually exist.

Working out teaches you persistence and delayed gratification. You learn that doing smaller things consistently will reap more results than doing big things spontaneously. You can work out three times every day for a week, and nothing will happen. But if you work out three times a week for even one or two months, you'll start to see changes. It isn't short bursts of motivation but years of dedication that reap results.

We often think of Christian development as a singular profound moment where we suddenly feel an intense spiritual connection unbeknownst to our former selves. But from the testimonies I usually hear, Christian growth happens in small incremental steps. It is the result of thousands of seemingly insignificant actions that when multiplied over time result in significant outcomes. Nobody becomes a bodybuilder after one trip to the gym but only after years of concentrated effort. Patiently sculpting your best body will teach you this.

Bodybuilding also leads to a lot of personal fulfillment. The body you attain cannot be bought, stolen, or inherited. It cannot be achieved without patience, and it cannot be maintained without passion. Bodybuilding is the best manifestation of your physical perfection. You grow in physical beauty and treat your body like a marble sculpture, intricately woven and carefully cut. Every feathering in the chest, every vein in the bicep, every striation in the shoulder, or every cut in the ab is something that you've worked for. The early 60s to late 80s, dubbed the "Golden Era" of bodybuilding emphasized this with people like Frank Zane and Bob Paris. Even if you don't go that far, there is still the idea that every pound you shed and every muscle you develop has been earned. You look at the before and after photos and see how you have control over it. Sure, some people were born with better genetics, but everyone is still capable of improving. It's not as though everyone can't still improve what they have been given. Nobody received creatine through the placenta; nobody was breastfed whey protein; you can always work out and become stronger than you currently are.

When you understand that you can change your body, you will understand that you can change other parts of your life. This is especially evident in your spiritual life. God's grace is everlasting and ultimately merciful. By acknowledging your weakness and bringing it to Christ, you allow His power to reside in you and make you stronger (2 Corinthians 12:9). He will help you change your life, somewhat the way a good trainer helps his athlete. Changing your body may help you understand that you can heal from your stage of brokenness and strengthen your weaknesses. How much more transformative can that change be with the direct power of the Almighty by your side?

Personally, it sometimes takes a lot of willpower for me to exercise. It is painful and hard, and many times I don't want to do it. It can be monotonous and strenuous. But I have to get used to being in pain and doing tedious hard work when I would sometimes rather not. All because there is a greater goal I am aiming at.

Reading the Bible or attending church services can sometimes feel similar to this. Sometimes I would rather binge my favorite action movie or TV show for the seventh time instead of going to church. But the anticipation of my heavenly Father telling me "Well done, good and faithful servant," at the end of it all makes every attempt and every sacrifice worthwhile. Bringing Him ultimate glory is what we are about.

Part III:
Masculine Christianity

CHAPTER 12
The Muscular Christian Model

———————————✕ ✕———————————

. . . a time to love and a time to hate, a time for war and a time for peace.
–Ecclesiastes 3:8

Whatever your hand finds to do, do it with all your might, . . .
–Ecclesiastes 9:10

I f you search for "Muscular Christianity" on the internet, you will
quickly find the name Theodore Roosevelt displayed as the mascot.
Roosevelt was a hunter, a writer, a reader, a soldier, and a US president.

Roosevelt was shot in the chest while campaigning in Milwaukee
for a third presidential term under his newly created Progressive Party.
The bullet pierced through a part of his glasses and a fifty-page copy of
his speech. Instead of going to the hospital, he proceeded to give a
ninety-minute speech with the bullet still lodged in his chest. Thanks
to his experience as an anatomist and a hunter, he figured that the bullet had not reached his lung and that he could wait to receive medical
treatment. After losing his third term bid, he set out on an expedition
to South America to traverse what he called the "River of Doubt." During his travels, he got injured and required surgery. He proceeded to
get a rag-tag, off-the-grid surgery and survived the procedure with no
anesthetic and without even flinching. The book aptly titled *River of
Doubt* talks about this expedition. At fifty years of age, he had vigor
and strength rare for someone half his age.

On the other hand, Theodore Roosevelt sported the nickname
"Teddy" Roosevelt. "Teddy" conjures imagery of a soft toy animal.
This is rather perplexing considering the descriptions of his strength

and power. Theodore was given this nickname because of an incident that occurred during a bear hunting trip in 1902. While on the trip, Roosevelt refused to shoot a bear that had been tied to a tree, considering it unsportsmanlike. As the story circulated, headlines began to call the story "Teddy's Bear" and that is why every cute stuffed bear is referred to as a "Teddy Bear." Theodore was a man of both rugged conviction and of compassion for mankind, animals, and nature.

Roosevelt said this to a group of men, which summarizes the Muscular Christian philosophy:

> When I speak of the American boy, what I say really applies to the grown-ups nearly as much as to the boys. . . . I want to see you game, boys; I want to see you brave and manly; and I also want to see you gentle and tender. In other words, you should make it your object to be the right kind of boys at home, so that your family will feel a genuine regret, instead of a sense of relief, when you stay away; and at the same time you must be able to hold your own in the outside world. You cannot do that if you have not manliness, courage in you. It does no good to have either of those two sets of qualities if you lack the other. I do not care how nice a little boy you are, how pleasant at home, if when you are out you are afraid of other little boys lest they be rude to you; for if so, you will not be a very happy boy nor grow up a very useful man. When a boy grows up, I want him to be of such a type that when somebody wrongs him, he will feel a good, healthy desire to show the wrong-doers that he cannot be wronged with impunity. I like to have the man who is a citizen feel, when a wrong is done to the community by anyone, when there is an exhibition of corruption or betrayal of

trust, or demagogy or violence, or brutality, not that he is shocked and horrified and would like to go home; but I want [him] to have him feel the determination to put the wrong-doer down, to make the man who does wrong aware that the decent man is not only his superior in decency, but his superior in strength.[1]

In the previous chapter, I explained Jack Donovan's cardinal virtues of a man. As a refresher, those are Strength, Courage, Mastery, and Honor.

Strength refers to how strong you are both physically and mentally. *Courage* is your ability to take risks and fight for yourself even when you are scared. *Mastery* is your ability to demonstrate proficiency in a given task. And *honor* is that feeling of accomplishment you get when people have acknowledged all the other traits.

These virtues, per Donavan, are the basic codes of manhood. Ancient Greek philosophers posited the ideal as something they called *arête.* This was the coupling of strength, virtue, courage, and character. *Arête* is a more advanced version of Donovan's virtue of mastery. It is the idea that a man must be ready wherever and whenever he is needed. In times of war, he ought to know how to fight and prevail. In times of peace, he ought to care for his family, keep his mind sharp, and serve his community and state. At all times a man is ready to serve in whatever capacity he is needed. He is a loving husband and father who can lead and serve in times of crisis at a moment's notice. He is a man who can both understand complex military tactics and survive the rigorous boot camp needed to be recruited. A man who practices *arête* is a man who is needed at all junctures of social community. *Arête* adds to Donavan's virtues by calling for every man to practice virtue in all he does.

Two different opposing types of men are all too commonly

portrayed in the media and it's worth pointing out here—the perennial clash between brains and brawn. The intellectual types will refer to the physically fit as meatheads. They think they are enlightened and that their intellect is superior to everyone else, superior especially to those who rely on their strength to accomplish anything. Likewise, the physically fit will insult the intellectuals, claiming that real men are those who fight fists to cuffs.

Both views are largely wrong, but each carries a kernel of truth. True excellence is found in the pursuit of excellence in all areas of life, in honing the mind and body cohesively, and acknowledging the fact that intellect, athletics, and morality must work together as one whole. This is the main tenet of Muscular Christianity.

This idea is best exemplified in the movie *Coach Carter*. Coach Carter is a biographical movie about a hoodlum basketball team that got a new coach and resulted in significant physical and personal growth for the team members. Their new coach, Coach Ken Carter, was markedly different from all the other coaches before him. What separated him from his predecessors was that he demanded respect, dignity, and excellence in all areas of life from all team members. From the get-go, Coach Carter told his students that "they will play like winners and act like winners." He directed that all team members must obtain at least a 2.3 GPA in their academics, not miss a single class, and always sit in the front seats in every class. Coach Carter even made them sign a contract saying they would abide by these rules. Up until this point, the players never cared about anything and were just messing around, being promiscuous, and involving themselves in gang activity. Coach Carter wanted to show them the right path to a holistically successful life. They were not used to this. Over the course of the movie, the coach earns their respect. Through a lot of heartfelt moments and heated story beats, all the students mature physically as well as personally.

In Richmond High School, before Coach Carter came along, only 50 percent of the students graduated. Of that 50 percent, most of whom were girls, only 6 percent of them continued to college. In Richmond, you were 80 percent more likely to go to prison than to college. But after Carter came and changed the environment, these men found hope. Coach Carter saved their lives. [2]

Conscientiousness and working with other people are essential skills for making it in life, not only on the basketball court. The players became better basketball players and better people due to Coach Carter's influence. He did a splendid job of instilling godly virtues in them.

The kids grew to become better at basketball, rather than fighting among themselves. They learned to be stronger mentally by going to every class and pushing through tough drills. They grew academically as well, each one meeting the 2.3 GPA standard. At the end, many of the players graduated, played college basketball, and got full time jobs. The players are now proper citizens, fully realized men. This is similar to how God, our ultimate spiritual coach, takes our otherwise erratic and messy lives and gives it order and direction.

I will end this chapter with a charge from the Stoic philosopher Epictetus from his book *The Art of Living: The Classical Manual on Virtue, Happiness and Effectiveness*:

> Now is the time to get serious about living your ideals. How long can you afford to put off who you really want to be? Your nobler self cannot wait any longer. Put your principles into practice—now. Stop the excuses and the procrastination. This is your life! You aren't a child anymore. The sooner you set yourself to your spiritual program, the happier you will be. The longer you wait, the more you'll be

vulnerable to mediocrity and feel filled with shame and re-gret, because you know you are capable of better. From this instant on, vow to stop disappointing yourself. Separate yourself from the mob. Decide to be extraordinary and do what you need to do—now.[3]

CHAPTER 13

Aggressive Christianity

———————————×( )×———————————

Physical training is of some value, but godliness has value for all things, holding promise for both the present life and the life to come.

–1 Timothy 4:8

. . . Don't be afraid of them. Remember the Lord, who is great and awesome, and fight for your families, your sons and your daughters, your wives and your homes.

–Nehemiah 4:14

The measure of a man is what he does with power.

–Plato

Speak softly and carry a big stick.

–Theodore Roosevelt

I love peace, but it is because I love justice and not because I am afraid of war.

–Theodore Roosevelt

There are many good things about physical fitness, but fitness holds promise only in this life and not in the next life. Our fitness goals should therefore be ordered not only towards ourselves but towards something beyond ourselves.

Many people have never gotten into body worship, but there are some who obsess over their physical fitness. They value their physical development more than their social or spiritual development.

In chapter 8 I covered how physical strength can be associated with social power and authority. That power ought to be used to protect the weak, not to oppress them. Power ought to be used to guard those

119

around you, to steer them in the right direction, to inspire them, and bring them closer to what is noble. The famous line from Spiderman, "With great power comes great responsibility," is just a catchy way of rephrasing Luke 12:48, "From everyone who has been given much, much will be demanded; and from the one who has been entrusted with much, much more will be asked."

Fitness should not be used to worship the self but as a means of worshipping God. It should be used as a way to protect and lead His people. When you look at fitness in the light of your Maker's purpose, you will see fitness not only as a higher physical imperative but also a spiritual tool for worship.

Contrary to the present-day social conscious, multiple studies by different psychologists have shown that having a father present in a child's life, especially a boy's life, reduces aggression as they grow older. Having a father present in a boy's life is one of the strongest predictors of empathy and self-control in his life.[1,2] Roughhousing (a.k.a. rough play) has been shown to support children's development. Part of the reason for this is that they teach boys how to control their strength. They understand just how strong they actually are when they can let that strength out in a controlled environment. When playing with their dad, they are made privy to the idea that someone can be an authoritative figure and use that immense power for something fun. In their book *The Art of Roughhousing: Good Old-Fashioned Horseplay and Why Every Kid Needs It*, DeBenedet and Cohen write that "when we roughhouse with our kids, we model for them how someone bigger and stronger holds back. We teach them self-control, fairness, and empathy."[3]

Exercise can teach you the same thing. If you understand how hard you can punch and if you have been punched hard yourself, you will know the kind of power that attack has, and you will understand how important it is to control it and how it should only be done in certain scenarios. You understand your capacity to hurt people with your power and strength. This is why police officers in training must first get tased themselves before they are allowed to use a taser on others. They have to understand the power of the tools they have before they are allowed to use them.

This reminds me of the concept of chivalry, a concept that is considered out of style in contemporary times. Headlines often scream, "Chivalry is dead." However, it was once in style, and it was there for a good, deep, and highly substantive reason. The meaning of chivalry has evolved, but its roots can be traced back to the crusades and knights era, between 1170 and 1220. We may unfortunately not wear knightly armor anymore, but its values are timeless. It instilled in men the virtues of nobility, humility, and courtesy. A cardinal character and responsibility of the knight was the protection of the weak, the orphan, the elderly, and women.

Chivalry is not about belittling women or any adjacent term we use these days; it is quite the opposite. It means cultivating a culture where men do not behave like ravenous beasts and shows that they have moved on from their primal dog-eat-dog, last-man-standing roots. Men are not to be unkempt animals and gruesome brutes. Chivalrous men are kind and loving people, protecting the weak and vulnerable wherever they find them. Being chivalrous means using your strength the way Christ did. He is our example.

The Passivity of Christianity

Some hold the view that Christianity is a passive religion that just gorged with the cultural flow. But this isn't true. As Christians, we are called to evangelize and fight for our faith. In the last section, I was deliberate about my choice of words. Strength, power, and authority are not very kind words, but they are necessary. Stronger and more powerful people should use their attributes for the good of all mankind. The Bible consistently teaches how to walk the fine line between abusing power and using it for good. Even beyond authority, the Bible demands perfect moderation and self-control. It tells us on the one hand not to be proud, and on the other hand not to cower in the face of evil. It tells us on one hand to respect authority, but on the other to change people's hearts.

Many hold a pacified idea of Jesus as a hippie. But no, Jesus was not passive towards evil and its corrosive elements. Jesus was stern and authoritative with evil. He did not tolerate sin. Jesus said He did not come to bring peace but to bring a sword—a sword to etch the line dividing good and evil. A sword to fight evil and oppression in His name.

We see this in the lives of the early disciples. Their gospel did not agree with the culture of their time. We may think that our present-day culture is bad, but in the times of the first disciples, the culture was arguably even more decadent. Still, they fought and challenged the status quo. Paul preached about sexual morality to the Greeks at the time when prostitution was commonplace.[4] There were far more "progressive" (by our standards) ideas and practices in the Bible than there are in our society now. Still, Christianity spread like wildfire in that early culture. This is because the gospel of Christianity is a perennial and eternal truth. The temporal ways of this culture and this life pale in comparison to the eternal truth found in Jesus Christ.

So don't roll over and let people walk on you. Thomas Aquinas put it well when he said that "a lack of the passion of anger is a vice."[5] If we love what is good, we need to also hate what is evil. A person who truly rejects evil feels anger toward it. We ought to show proper vitriol in the face of evil because it threatens what is good. We often say that we should hate the sin but love the sinner. These are not two disconnected statements; they are necessary parts of each other. The full spectrum of emotions can be good when properly utilized.

Avatar: The Last Airbender portrays fire as the element of destruction. But as the show progresses, we learn that fire is really the wellspring of all human passion. Oftentimes that passion is used to harm and oppress other people, but it does not have to be used in this way. General Iroh, the wise mentor character, demonstrates that passion can be used to bear good fruit by demonstrating intense enthusiasm, an unwavering heart, and unconditional love.[6] Similar to anger, fire is a double-edged sword. It is raw energy that can be used for good and for bad.

Meekness is a Christian virtue often confused with subservience. I think that it is better understood in the way Aristotle defines it in his *Nichomachean Ethics*. The *praus* person, (the meek person) is the one who feels anger on the right grounds, against the right person, in the right manner, at the right moment, for the right amount of time.[7] Meekness is strength contained and controlled. It is carrying a sword and keeping it sheathed. It is having a feral ferocity capable of overwhelming anyone—yet having the self-control to refrain from using an iota more than necessary. And the word for meek or meekness in the Bible, to many people's surprise, is completely in line with this understanding. This is the kind of strength sports help to cultivate. This is why the Bible describes Moses as a meek man even though he stood against Pharaoh in the name of his God, even though he argued with God, and even though he effectively led the Israelites in the wilderness for forty years. Jesus, our sinless, powerful, and fearless savior, also describes Himself as meek and humble of heart. As I will explain later, He was always in perfect control of His anger.

Part of the reason people believe Christianity is a wimpy religion is that godly commands like "judge not" and "love thy neighbor" have been used to mischaracterize Christianity. Famous philosophers, most notably Friedrich Nietzsche, have criticized the religion for being such, even going as far as to call it an exercise in "self-mutilation." He said, "From the beginning, Christian faith has been sacrifice: sacrifice of all freedom, of all pride, of all self-confidence of the spirit; it is simultaneously enslavement and self-derision, self-mutilation."[8] Nietzsche believed that in life, people abide by either "slave morality" or "master morality." Sitting at the top of society are the masters. The masters assert their will on the world by exercising their strength and are glorified for their strength. The masters create their own morality and enforce it on others. At the bottom of society are the slaves. These are timid, spineless, and pacified people who have been emasculated by their masters into not being able to assert their will. The slaves cope with their insignificance by asserting that it is actually more righteous and virtuous to be weak and submissive. They are unable to get respect, so instead of demanding respect and justice, they claim they are practicing forgiveness; instead of acquiring wealth, they condemn it and call it greed. Seeking glory and fame, to them, is narcissism; being oppressed is being obedient; being strong and taking what you want is wrath. The moral slave will not even attempt to take power for this very reason.

Nietzsche's description is perhaps the most vivid articulation of the passivity ascribed to Christianity. It is important to note that Nietzsche and those who subscribe to his worldview believe that passivity is fundamental to Christianity and that it is not some unfortunate by-product. This philosophical idea is perhaps what has turned many people away from Christianity.

I am convinced that this interpretation of passivity as a Christian trait is mostly a misunderstanding of certain verses in Scripture that guide Christians in their relationships, mostly (but not exclusively) from Jesus' Sermon on the Mount. Throughout the sermon, Jesus brings up certain Mosaic laws and emphasizes the spirit behind the laws, not the rigid, legal application that the Jews were practicing. He says He came to fulfill the Law by giving it its ultimate and divine interpretation, not to destroy it.

With this in mind, let us review some of the Bible's popular teachings.

Turn the Other Cheek

In Matthew 5:38–42 we read,

You have heard that it was said, 'Eye for eye, and tooth for tooth.' But I tell you, do not resist an evil person. If anyone slaps you on the right cheek, turn to them the other cheek also. And if anyone wants to sue you and take your shirt, hand over your coat as well. If anyone forces you to go one mile, go with them two miles. Give to the one who asks you, and do not turn away from the one who wants to borrow from you.

A common view of "turn the other cheek" is to be a spineless doormat, to let your enemy continuously walk all over you, to slap you around, to not demand even the slightest respect, and to only wait for God to judge them. This is fundamentally different from the Mosaic law of "an eye for an eye." Indeed, this would go against a lot of what Moses did in his own life. Should Moses have let the Israelites continue to be taken advantage of by Pharaoh? Was God being inconsistent when He told Moses to fight back against Pharaoh? Should Jesus have let the Pharisees continue being hypocrites and allowed them to walk all over Him instead of calling them "snakes," "vipers," and "children of hell?" Was Jesus being a hypocrite? Did God change His mind on one of His moral principles? One part of Scripture calls for His followers to be spat on, while the other calls for equal justice. Since Jesus came to fulfill the Law, not do away with it, I do not think that He wants His followers to ask for more abuse when they are abused.

The big picture here is about taking revenge for wrongs suffered. I believe that when He said to turn the other cheek, He wants us to boldly stand up to our abusers and confront them as equals. Striking back at your abuser only serves to perpetuate the evil behavior, not stop it. It doesn't change the hearts of those who wrong you. That's why immediately after, Jesus says that we should not love our neighbor and hate our enemy, but we should love our enemy and pray for them. The macro idea Jesus is getting at is that it's more important to change the hearts of people (to win spiritually) than it is to physically dominate them (to win physically). God could send angels to force us to obey Him at sword point, but He is more concerned with genuinely changing our hearts. We ultimately don't win with fear, but with love. When you turn the other cheek, you are not being a doormat, you are actually bravely standing your ground, you are countering bullying from a position of strength. The person who, when being reviled, stands their ground, stares their reviler straight in the eye, and asks them, "Are you done?" will make the abuser look foolish and hopefully cause them to think of his actions in shame and regret.

That is not being a doormat. That is being brave and stopping the abuse right there. Martin Luther King Jr., at times, demonstrated turning the other cheek through his non-violent protests against discriminatory laws. Instead of fighting back, he stood his ground in a brave act of defiance, daring his enemies to show even more of their true colors. By doing this, he was awarded with public applause. He turned the other cheek, and by doing so, he was effective in stopping the cycle of oppression against black people in the United States. When Jesus said to turn the other cheek, He meant that believers should stand their ground against evil, that their actions will speak loudly for them. Jesus wants us to act patiently and be more concerned with changing people's hearts than with giving people what they deserve.

The biblical scholar Walter Wink, in *Engaging the Powers: Discernment and Resistance in a World of Domination*, gives one interpretation of how this verse ought to be read, given its audience and time period. To the Jewish audience Jesus was speaking to, slapping someone on the right cheek was to have someone use the back of their right hand to slap you. This was a demonstration of superiority. It's how they punish inferiors. Jesus tells us to turn the other cheek. This means that they would have to use their palm, their other hand, or their fist to punch you. Using the palm or the fist would be an acknowledgment of them being an equal. Using your left hand to backhand them was taboo because it was seen as unclean. People would literally clean their poop with that hand so no one would ever use it.[9] So in the context of the verse, according to Walter Wink, Jesus is telling you to passively and cleverly demand respect from an ostensible position of weakness. Even selling the cloak and going the extra mile was seen as a passive act of defiance. To give them your cloak meant that you would walk around naked and that would reflect poorly on the master. If someone forces you to carry their burden for one mile, going another would make the oppressor look lazy and get them punished.

Another interpretation I have heard for this verse is that it refers to personal slights against you. You should be a doormat when someone slights you personally, but the rules don't apply when people spit on those close to you or when people spit on God.

In my view, all these interpretations are true to some degree. It is true that we may sometimes be in positions where we really do just have to take the mockery and even beatings the world throws at us with stoic dignity. Sometimes it truly is the best course of action. But ultimately,

I believe that the large picture of this verse is that we should be primarily concerned with changing the hearts of those who treat us poorly. Thus, standing up for your human dignity while making your oppressors look bad in a non-confrontational way is a very strong strategy. However, at the same time, you cannot ignore the times when Jesus Himself would publicly criticize His enemies, and we know He was physically confrontational on at least one occasion. He also told his disciples to sell their garments to buy swords. Thus, if I had to summarize my view, it is that we should prioritize non-confrontation, but if confrontation is what will ultimately change the most number of people's hearts, if we can reasonably conclude that confrontation will maximize goodness, then it is permissible.

If the idea of using violence in the name of Jesus to handle confrontations makes you upset, then this is all the more reason to pursue Muscular Christianity. Large muscles aren't just for show, they can be a legitimate deterrent to violence. Nobody wants to fight a bodybuilder, even if the bodybuilder doesn't know how to fight.

Isn't Killing Against the Bible?

I will take a small departure from the Sermon on the Mount to talk about Exodus 20:13. In most versions of the Bible, it never says killing is wrong. The reason many people think otherwise is because the King James Version says, "Thou shalt not kill." However, most scholars agree that Exodus 20:13 more accurately says that you shall not "murder," not you shall not "kill." The definition of murder according to the Merriam-Webster dictionary is "to kill (a person) unlawfully and unjustifiably with premeditated malice"[10] In Genesis and Exodus, God killed people outright. In Joshua, and 1 Samuel, God aided the Hebrews in sacking Jericho, and He aided David in slaying Goliath. Even though the latter two examples are of killing by man and not by God, they were not considered murder, for the lives taken were not innocent and thus they were justified by God. Accidental killing would also be absolved because there is no premeditated malice therefore it should not be judged the same as intentional killing.

Don't Judge

This is an often-misunderstood phrase from the Sermon on the Mount. It is perhaps the most quoted and misunderstood verse in contemporary times. It is not uncommon to hear people say, "the Bible is about loving, not judging!" First of all, we must acknowledge that it is impossible to go about life without judging. Judging merely means forming an opinion or having a belief. In fact, the phrase "you shouldn't judge" is itself a judgment because it is your belief that we should not have beliefs. Typically, when people say that we shouldn't judge, they are really saying that we should not voice our opinion about a specific issue. That may be a good or a bad thing. It depends on the context.

Now that we have that minor technicality out of the way, let's tackle the quote again. "The Bible is about loving, not judging!" is a false dichotomy. Just because someone judges your actions in the light of facts and established truth does not mean they don't love you. A parent must tell a child what is right and what is wrong and guide the kid to distinguish between the two. This is a form of judgment, and it is actually good. Some people object to the entire premise and say, "God doesn't judge," but that is also wrong. The entire Bible is filled with God judging people. Turn to any page in the Bible, and I mean almost any page, and you will see God judging, or someone referencing God judging the people of the world.

If you look through the entire Bible, you will certainly find one instance of the word "judge" immediately followed by the word "not."

If you go to Bible.com and search "don't judge," you will find a part of a Bible verse that tells you not to judge. But that phrase is often espoused bereft of all context. The complete quote from Jesus' Sermon on the Mount is as follows: "Do not judge, or you too will be judged. For in the same way you judge others, you will be judged, and with the measure you use, it will be measured to you. Why do you look at the speck of sawdust in your brother's eye and pay no attention to the plank in your own eye?" (Matthew 7:1–3).

This verse is saying don't judge someone in a way you are not willing to be judged. Someone once told me that the best advice you can give to yourself is the advice you give others. Jesus was speaking to hypocrites who in one breath tell people to do one thing and in the other breath do the opposite. Jesus isn't telling us *not* to judge, He's telling us *how* to judge. There is actually another verse where Jesus explicitly commands His disciples to judge others. In John 7:24 He tells them "stop judging by mere appearances, but instead judge correctly." So do not be afraid to take a stand for righteousness. That is what this command is about.

Those Who Live by the Sword Die by the Sword

Living by the sword does not mean that you can never use the sword. If that were so, the Bible would have taught that war was wrong. But nowhere in the Bible does it ever say that war in itself is wrong. I'll expand on that point later in the chapter.

Before Peter cut off Malchus's ear, Jesus told the disciples to buy swords. Jesus knew this would happen yet still told the disciples to buy swords. The swords were not for Himself, He could call twelve legions of angels to protect Him. The swords were for the disciples' own sake. After Peter cuts his ear, Jesus doesn't tell Peter to throw his sword away, He just tells Peter to put it *back in its place*. The swords weren't just for show, they were there to be used for the right reason, against the right person, in the right manner, at the right moment. Now was not that moment. Peter used the sword out of passion. I think that in context, this verse is saying that if you live with a passion for violence, you will die in the passion of violence.

Love Your Neighbor

We absolutely should be loving our neighbors and those around us because they are God's creation. However, loving them doesn't mean affirming everything they do. This is the mistake a lot of Christians make. We say that we should love each other, and while that is a true and crowd-pleasing message, it doesn't actually mean much if we don't go further. When Christians say "love," the idea people have is that we should all just hold hands and think generally nice things about each other. That sort of messaging is completely insufficient in today's culture. People need to understand what Christian love actually is.

To love, according to Thomas Aquinas, is to "will the good of the other." To will the good of others, from a Christian standpoint, would be to help them come closer to God and to point them away from sin. If that means that they won't like you, then so be it. If my friend is addicted to drugs, helping them break their addiction instead of condoning their drug use and affirming their desires, is the loving thing to do. This is the Christian way. Making a child eat their vegetables instead of a dish of candy in order to make sure they grow up strong and healthy is a way of loving them, even if the child doesn't like it. Loving someone doesn't necessarily mean that the person you love will like everything you do to them. We confuse the two a lot. I sometimes wonder if Christians actually know what "love" means, or if they choose to prevaricate so as to not stir conflict.

It is true and wonderful how Jesus, someone who is perfect in every way, humbled Himself to live among sinners like us. But He didn't come to accept and affirm everything we believed. He came to call us to be better and more virtuous, to transform us, and to live for Him. Just like a doctor healing his patients. If someone is sick, a doctor doesn't just sit there and affirm their sickness, they will diagnose it and try to heal them. Even if they are not yet ill but are indulging in unhealthy habits that will lead to illness, the doctor will warn them about these habits and show them how to fix their lives. That is how we ought to be with our neighbors. We should love and accept them as fearfully and wonderfully made creatures of the Almighty God—but not accept everything they do. We should try to help them fix their flaws.

Still, on the perceived passivity of Christianity, the Bible is full of powerful accounts of how God uses weak and broken people for His glory. It's amazing how He fixes and strengthens them. Saul was murdering Christians until he met God—who forgave him, empowered him, changed his name to Paul, and raised him to be one of the most influential biblical figures ever. David was a young shepherd boy whom God used to take out the giant Goliath. Moses was an old man and a stammerer when God used him to speak to Pharoah and to lead the Jews from Egyptian bondage. Yes, God uses us despite our weakness but that does not give us a license to stay weak. Those figures became more powerful and more influential once they became stronger in their faith. So will you.

People who see Jesus as a soft-spoken and caring man are not wrong at all. I'm not saying that there isn't a place and time to be kind and compassionate, especially when conversing with people on a personal level, but that is just telling one part of the story. The teacher who told His disciples to love their neighbor counter-balanced this by publicly calling His critics dogs. The Man who told us to care for the poor wrecked a temple that vendors were trading at. He even fashioned a whip to drive the moneychangers out of the Temple. So, Jesus wasn't always polite, and He certainly didn't tolerate evil. He was sometimes impolite and was always intolerant of evil.

If you remove the name "Jesus" from some of these biblical texts, many Christians may read His actions and words and think this man was acting in a manner that is un-Christlike. They would wag their finger and say, "No! God just wants us to be nice to people!" But the Bible doesn't call us to do that. Jesus didn't shy away from harsh truths. He was crucified for stirring up controversy in the name of truth. All because He loved us. He would not have been crucified if His ultimate message were to tell us all to be nice. Being assertive, using harsh words in the face of wicked evil, showing anger at sin, and turning tables are not un-Christlike. In fact, they are precisely Christlike.

Call Things What They Are

In our culture, we are generally terrified to call out sin for what it is. The media personality Andrew Tate cites this as one of the reasons he left Orthodox Christianity and converted to Islam. But the Bible doesn't support this. John the Baptist was beheaded by King Herod because he called out his sin, and yet in Matthew 11 Jesus called him the greatest man to ever be born of a woman. If that isn't a neon-light, glowing endorsement of John's actions, then I don't know what is. The greatest man in the world was someone who died because he denounced evil.

In Revelation 2, John writes to the angel of the church in Ephesus. He denounces the church for forsaking love and speaks of how they have fallen. But he says they have one thing in their favor in that they hated evil practices. Their one saving grace is that they at least have an appropriate level of hatred for evil practices.

I am not saying that we should purposefully go out, look for trouble, and play bingo with every instance of sin we see. We shouldn't be out looking for fights or getting needlessly confrontational, but we should defend the faith and preach the correct gospel no matter what. Romans 12:18 is a good verse to keep in mind. It says, "If it is possible, as far as it depends on you, live at peace with everyone." Paul doesn't say, "Live peaceably at all costs." The gospels contain non-negotiable biblical values. Some people will be hostile towards it and that will inspire conflict. If confrontation comes up, do what you need to do. If sin is shamelessly being celebrated, do what you need to do. I am merely saying that we shouldn't be afraid of the world or be unnecessarily belligerent towards it.

Dude, Jesus dropped like one commandment on us man, it's all about spreading peace and letting people be. It's called being a decent human being.

Just gotta ride that vibe of being kinda nice according to whatever's cool in our time while ignoring that outdated rulebook. Then boom! You're totally doing the wholesome Christianity, my friend. 🤙💚

This meme demonstrates what many Christians think our mission is.

I would go as far as to argue that conflict can actually be a good thing. Christians are very conflict avoidant, but what tends to happen is when conflict is temporarily avoided, it becomes delayed and magnified. When you refrain from actively engaging with others, it can foster an atmosphere of elitism, implicitly suggesting a sense of superiority and disdain towards those being ignored. This attitude may be interpreted as a condescending message, as if stating, "We consider ourselves superior to your feeble existence. Remain in your lowly state, you pitiful creatures, as we are beyond your reach."

This is what I believe has played a part in the decline of Christianity in recent years. It's the classic story of pride leading to one's downfall, only this time it's a whole religion. Too many people I know grew up in religious cultures where they were secluded from the rest of the world, and when they left that bubble, they became worldly. I am not saying that Christians need to fully immerse themselves in the world's affairs and in the prevailing culture, but we should be aware of what is happening around us and develop clear arguments in response to whatever influence they may have on society.

Nevertheless, there are many modern Christians who have acquiesced to the ways of the world to such an extent that they don't even believe that Christianity is in intense confrontation with the ways of the world. In their bid to be seen as nice and "loving" people, they have adopted revisionist theology in order to conform to the sensibilities of contemporary culture. Little wonder the world is confused about the Christian message.

Righteous Anger

The Bible calls us to exhibit righteous anger. Not anger when we lose in a video game or when someone cuts us off in traffic, but indignation when we see evil things that offend God. In Matthew 18:6, Jesus uses morbid and violent imagery when saying it would be better to drown in the sea with a stone around your neck than to harm a child. Had our contemporary Christians been around two thousand years ago, I'm sure they'd go on The Sticks and Stones News broadcast, shaking their heads and telling Jesus that Jesus would never say what Jesus said. They would tell Christ that Christianity has no place for that kind of language. But yes, this is within the realm of Christianity. Christianity calls us to practice meekness and tenderness and balance that with justified aggression.

The Biblical scholar Paul Gondreau, in *The Passions of Christ's Soul in the Theology of St. Thomas Aquinas*, points out five explicit mentions of Jesus's anger and *at least* twenty-five implicit mentions of Jesus's anger, frustration, or indignation in the Bible. In his words, "the Gospels testify more towards Jesus's anger than any other emotion."[11] Anger when moderated by meekness is a human emotion God gave us that provides us with the energy to virtuously tackle what is sinful. We use meekness to harnesses the passion of anger unto the good of reason. Just as Jesus did.

Slave Morality Examined

Jesus doesn't want us to stay at the same level, pretending that it is some sort of virtue. In the parable of the talents, Jesus tells a story of a master who gives one servant five talents, another two talents, and the other one talent to trade with. The servant who is given five talents doubles his talents, the servant who has two talents also doubles his talents, and the servant who is given one talent just hides it under his mattress. When confronted by their master, those who sought to multiply their talents are praised and even called "good and faithful servants." The servant who buried his talent for fear of his master is scorned by his master.

Jesus doesn't want us to stay in the same place and never move forward, take risks, and become stronger. Jesus never sees being weak or not working towards and striving to be your best as a virtue. He calls us to be strong and to fight for His truth and to work toward being our best and not be afraid of conflict or challenging the status quo. Upon further examination, it actually may seem that Jesus constantly teaches the opposite of slave morality.

Yet I don't want to paint the picture that Christianity has no elements of so-called slave morality. While Christians assert a morality, it is only the morality that is already in the Bible, not their own made-up morality. That is a key difference. Beyond that, as Christians, we are called to forgive instead of avenge, to be generous instead of miserly.

Jesus dying on the cross could be seen as the quintessential example of slave morality. He could've stopped Himself from dying, but He didn't. Instead, He prayed, "Father, forgive them, for they do not know what they are doing" (Luke 23:34). He asked God to forgive His killers instead of punishing them. What makes this different, however, is that while Jesus *could* have sent angels to save His life and send everyone else to hell, He *didn't.* He also knew that He would be rising back from the dead, which would ultimately lead to more goodness than if He didn't.

Slaves have no power and mask that as a virtue. Jesus had power but chose not to use it. Jesus's action on the cross was not a sign of weakness but an act of impossible strength. It seems that Nietzsche failed to consider the idea that someone could have power, yet choose to exercise it in a loving way. Nietzsche would likely think of chastity as a form of slave morality, and that people who are unable to find a mate mask that insecurity by calling it purity and a virtue. However, if you are capable of attracting a mate but choose not to do so in order to remain sexually pure, you have demonstrated a higher act of strength than finding a mate on its own. In my opinion, the highest order of virtue isn't avoiding evil, it's having the choice to do evil and choosing good instead. I believe you are most virtuous when you have the ability to exploit opportunities but choose not to do it for a higher purpose.

It shows you have an iron will, dedication, and commitment to something beyond earthly passions.

Another problem with Nietzsche's critique is that it assumes being wealthy, for example, is good in itself. It's quite clear that that isn't the case. Overly wealthy people oftentimes have worse mental health issues than others; it's usually the moderately wealthy people that are the happiest. The people who make just enough money to where they don't need to worry about their immediate needs anymore are often happier than the ultra-rich. Consider how winning the lottery has ruined many lives. Indeed, it seems as though no matter how you slice it, you need virtue and discipline in life. That will always be more important than any material good we can possess by exercising master morality.

To be meek, as a reminder, is to exercise no more power than necessary and to contain and control that power; and this assumes that you have the power to begin with. Still, to have power and exercise it righteously could perhaps be seen as a form of slave morality. If that's your argument, then sure. But if that's the case, then one can argue that being a slave is not always a bad thing.

Christians don't see the necessity of excessive material wealth. At the core of Christianity, we are not living for this world but for heaven. Therefore, giving in to earthly passions when it distracts you from what is ultimately more important is a terrible mistake.

In a literal sense, the Bible speaks a lot about whether you are a slave or a master and how there is power in both positions. In the popular cartoon *Avatar: The Last Airbender*, there is a wise old character by the name of Iroh. He was born into royalty. He was born heir to the throne and was meant to be the man glorified for putting an end to the almost century-long war between four tribes. A series of events happened that demoted this once-royal military leader to a begging peasant. Through all of this, he stayed strong and never saw his situation as hopeless. He understood that whether you are royalty or a commoner, you can still find joy and fulfillment in life.[12]

If Nietzsche had used slave and master morality terms to describe not Jesus but modern Christianity, I think he would be on the right track. Contemporary Christians have accepted a lot of worldly attacks, just as Jesus did. But it is not as though we aren't fighting back because we are suffering with dignity and cooking something up that will lead to more goodness in the future. Too many of us aren't fighting back because we are toothless cowards who don't have the moral courage to fight, all the while pretending that this weakness is actually a sign of virtue.

Power

We are all equal under God, but that doesn't mean we all have equal influence. He will judge us all with the same standard, but that doesn't mean we don't play different roles. God chose Moses and Abraham to lead the Israelites, and Jesus chose Peter to be the leader of the disciples. In our time, the pastor leads the church and thus holds the most influence. For Catholics, the Pope is the leader of the universal church.

The Bible isn't against the use of hierarchies or authorities. Power just needs to be used wisely to direct people in a righteous way. We can be right and speak the truth, but if we do not have the power to properly disseminate that truth, our words effectively mean nothing. Sometimes we must be more authoritative and use that to guide people in the right direction, to try to make them realize the errors of their ways. Some of us will be leaders and some will be followers. Whatever role you play, play it with grace. In the fight to promote the gospel, there may be times when you do not have an option other than enduring worldly attacks. For Jesus and for people enduring similarly tempestuous environments, there is no other way. If this happens, of course, we should respond with the grace Christ shows to us. But also, when we can, we ought to destroy evil. 2 Corinthians 10:1-6 echoes a similar sentiment. It talks about becoming virtuous, being bold, and using spiritual power to demolish evil. Use the power you have to promote as much goodness as possible. With that in mind, let's look at how we ought to respond to one of the most extreme acts of human evil. Let's look at war and violence.

War and Violence

War is perhaps man's most violent and barbaric act. It is where two or more parties have reached such a passionate point of disagreement that they physically attack each other to get what they want. Christianity has a long history of war and violence, whether that be in Bible times or during the Crusades. But what exactly does the Bible teach, and what do Christian thinkers say on the issue?

For starters, we must understand that the Bible does not make any attempt to glorify killing people for no good reason. David killed Goliath, and it was seen as an inspirational victory, but not because David was a powerful figure who could kill anyone standing in his path. Rather, it was a demonstration of his trust in God and his determination to overcome his people's subjugation by their Philistine enemies. We learn from this that the Bible sees violence sometimes as a necessary part of life, but it is still nothing to be glorified. In fact, many verses in the Bible condemn violence. Psalm 11:5 outright condemns the wicked man who enjoys violence. It says, "The LORD examines the righteous, but the wicked, those who love violence, He hates with a passion." The lesson for us in this is that violence is something we should only engage in when absolutely necessary.

In the anime *Vinland Saga*, a character named Thors illustrates this. Thors grew up as a warrior and became the greatest warrior of his time. But he understood that war and violence weren't the greatest good, so he abandoned his Viking life for a modest, peaceful life. This was a shock to everyone because the Viking culture of his time glorified conquest and violence above everything. So for Thors, who was the best of the warriors to reject that calling was for him to stand diametrically opposed to everything his society stood for and everything he excelled at. But Thors understood modest, cherishable things to be ultimately more important than war, and that the glory he got through conquest was fickle. The only reason we saw him ever pick up his sword again was to protect his family when there was no other option.[13]

Thors' story is in line with Christian teachings. St. Augustine outlined what has been dubbed the "Just War Theory." In it he states that war is justified and could in fact be a good thing if it meets the following criteria:

- The war is for a just cause.

- Engaging in the war has a reasonable chance of victory.

- The war is for the right intention.

- The war cry is from a legitimate authority.

- The acts taken in war must be of a proportional response.

- The war's outcome will be a superior situation than if it never happened.

- The war is a last resort.[14]

St. Augustine's criteria above should help people understand the times when Christians have had to resort to violence. Violence isn't to be used to move the kingdom of God. But sometimes, violence is the only way to reasonably preserve yourself. If you are in the military or if you are a police officer, there are times when you need to be violent to do your work. Those are seen as good, even noble professions. There are Christians who believe that while those occupations are necessary, they are still unbecoming for a Christian to participate in. To that, I would have to respectfully disagree. If something is necessary and even noble for a non-believer to do, that standard also ought to be applied to Christians. They aren't suddenly no longer noble when a Christian does it.

The Bible never says that war is wrong. If anything, it affirms that there is a time and place for it. When John was preparing the way for Jesus, some soldiers asked John how they could live a virtuous life, and John never told them to stop being soldiers. This would have been the perfect time for him to give the dictum of Christian pacifism, but he didn't. He just said, "Don't extort money and don't accuse people falsely—be content with your pay" (Luke 3:14). In Psalm 144:1 it actually tells you to train your hands for war and ready your fingers for battle. Paul also uses soldier life as a metaphor for spiritual life. If being a soldier was sinful, it is unlikely that it would be used as a metaphor for anything good. In Revelation, it also talks about how Jesus himself will be carrying a sword when He comes back (Revelation 1:16).

Violence can be justified if it is needed to protect those around you or yourself in the face of injustice. It could be the most immediate defense we have to offer. Ideally, you should try to handle every situation in a calm and diplomatic manner, but this isn't always possible. Many Christians tend to think that the aggressive approach, no matter what, always, invariably, absolutely, every time, in every scenario, in every event, without fail or exception, is the wrong choice. But there are scenarios where the aggressive, even physically violent approach, is not only valid but ideal. Take the Greenwood Park Mall, Indiana, shooting incident in 2022. Three people were killed, and two others were injured in the shooting before the perpetrator was fatally shot by twenty-two-year-old Elisjsha Dicken, a legally armed civilian bystander. This was the necessary, aggressive, and correct response.

Violence for Entertainment

We shouldn't bask in gore for its own sake. Remember what I said about meekness, how we ought to use no more force than necessary. The violence in the movie *Saving Private Ryan* or the TV series *Invincible* are certainly gory, but it is not gratuitous. And we are not meant to gawk at them or watch them simply for the sake of seeing the gore. In *Saving Private Ryan,* the point of the violence and gore is to show what these men faced and overcame. It's supposed to highlight the reality of their situation. The violence is used to highlight the plight they faced on D-Day. In *Invincible,* the violence is used to show just how dark and gory a realistic superhero story would be.

Is it sinful, then, to watch or participate in combat sports like MMA or boxing? Maybe, maybe not. I will share some considerations you must make when addressing the issue.

Most of these sports are entertainment. In the case of MMA, the competitors agree to the fight and accept the risks. If the fighters have hatred in their hearts and genuinely want to kill their opponents, not in the rivalry competition sense but in a "I hate you and want to murder you" sense, that would be wrong. Malice is bad, but a competitive spirit is good. Combat sports even have rules for mediating how much violence you can use in a fight. For example, boxers must actually be boxing and not wrestling (although with the way they like to hug each other you may wonder). Judo competitions don't allow you to bite your opponent. Karate competitions don't allow you to carry weapons. These are sports, structured outlets for people to have fun and let out their aggression. They are a raw demonstration of strength, speed, technique, coordination, and flexibility. We have an intrinsic appreciation for these demonstrations of human capabilities.

Think about it like the difference between kids roughhousing versus kids bullying. The former is all in good fun and to get out some aggression, and we stop before it goes too far. The latter is aimed at making the other person suffer. To take pleasure in bullying is perverse and unacceptable.

With these extremely violent sports, however, you must still grapple with the fact that you are watching or perhaps participating in a sport of intentionally pummeling and injuring someone. The entire goal of these sports is to pummel and injure. If you are a participant, you must consider if it is possible to do so while still glorifying God. Some would argue that it is not okay to injure God's creation for material gain. They would say that these sports are akin to self-abuse because at some point, you will surely get seriously injured. Can this be done with respect to God's teaching? You decide.

In my opinion, I don't think the injury and harm with these sports are severe enough to warrant the sport being judged sinful. They are not like the popular conception of olden-day gladiator battles, where the death of one participant was normal. There is also a difference between taking the risk of getting hurt as a byproduct and intentionally hurting yourself through self-abuse. In one case, you are not trying to injure, but you understand that injury may happen; you are willing to take the risk. In the other case, you are actively trying to make it happen.

Fighting can also instill a lot of great values, which I have made note of in previous chapters. Physical pain can be analogous to emotional or spiritual pain, which can help you bounce back stronger. Many fighters are notoriously underpaid, implying they do it because they really love it. It is the love of the sport over everything. They don't fight for the money. They do it because it is extremely invigorating.

There's a primal rush that kicks in during combat. In a literal sense, people who fight are motivated by the fundamental masculine drive to prove they are the strongest and stand at the top of the dominance hierarchy. The proceeding mastery of those drives is highly rewarding and is character-building. Similar to my discussion on performance-enhancing drugs, however, I do believe that there is a rational argument to be made either way.

When it comes to the choreographed fights seen in *Marvel, anime*, and (if you're super cool) *online stickman animations*, they are simulated violence and not the real thing. It is actually the choreography and animation that we are enjoying. As in martial arts, superheroes show off their strength, coordination, speed, and flexibility to impressive degrees. In the fictional fights, they show this off in ways that we cannot even conceptualize. We can understand punches and kicks, but we cannot understand laser beams and buildings being thrown across the battlefield. There are often narrative reasons for the violence in these shows and movies. We rejoice when the villain loses, and we feel a cathartic release within us when we see it physically happen.

Even though we know it's not real life, when a character goes overkill and makes the opponent excessively suffer, we feel uncomfortable. In the anime *Naruto*, in the "Forest of Death." Sasuke, one of the characters we are rooting for, recovers from near death and obtains a new power. We are excited to see him come back and win, but it quickly becomes uncomfortable to watch. This is because he starts to abuse his enemy ninjas more than he needs to. In a scene that can only be described as bone-chilling, he savagely stands on top of an opponent's back, grabs his arms, and over-extends the shoulder joints, dislocating them in the process. The opponent is so utterly outclassed that to call him a punching bag for Sasuke would be a giving him too much credit.[15] It would be an insult to all the punching bags around the world to compare them to him. At least punching bags don't click and pop and cry out of sheer agony. It was overkill and brutal. Taking pleasure in savagely beating up weaker people is not fun to watch.

If you are one of those who see Christianity as a passive religion, I hope that in this chapter, I have given you a few things to think about that might convince you otherwise.

CHAPTER 14
Atrophied Christianity

So God created mankind in his own image, in the image of God He created them;
male and female He created them.
–Genesis 1:27

...we are more than conquerors through him who loved us.
–Romans 8:37

Manhood is the social barrier that societies must erect against entropy,
human enemies, the forces of nature, time,
and all the human weaknesses that endanger group life.
–David D. Gilmore

Men are of indispensable importance to the growth of the church, which makes their lack of attendance very worrisome. Depending somewhat on the denomination, if you look closely at most churches now, you will find more women than men. Research has found that women make up roughly 53 percent of Christianity worldwide.[1] In the USA however, women make up 61 percent of Christianity.[2] This is troubling for the USA (and the entire Western world) because male church attendance seems to correlate better with offspring church attendance than female church attendance does. Children are ten times more likely to be regular churchgoers if the dad takes an active part in their faith.[3] If we are to grow Christianity, we need more men. In some churches, there doesn't seem to be a notable gap at all, but in others the gap is considerably wider.

I find this odd because in my circles I often hear about how sexist the Bible is. Whenever the Bible is talking about women and even utters the word "submission," all of my atheist friends collectively jump into an agitated frenzy. First-generation feminists even went as far as to assert that the Bible and the Church are the biggest roadblocks to women's equality.[4] Yet, weirdly enough, there are more women than men in churches.

The zeitgeist of modern Christianity has undoubtedly rung a patriarchal tone. Christianity was by and large developed by men. You won't find too many prominent female figures in the Bible, at least in comparison to men. In our society, which prices the equal representation of the sexes at a premium, it highlights just how perplexing it is to see that there is a gender gap in favor of women in the church.

This gender gap in Christianity most likely existed before the feminist revolution. Catholic author Leon J. Poddles dates the gap to the thirteenth century. In the United States it existed in the seventeenth century when the Puritan settlers entered the country.[5]

Despite its male promulgators, Christianity is seen by many as a soft and effeminate religion. Softness is associated more with women than with men. Perhaps because of this, women make up a larger portion of the church; therefore, Christianity is presented on the macroscale in a way that conforms to female sensibilities.

To give just one example, the anime *Vinland Saga* is a tale about Vikings going from land to land stealing goods, conquering lands, and doing archetypal Viking things. One of the characters, Thorkell, is a quintessential icon of eleventh-century Viking masculinity, sporting large muscles, Viking attire, and a whimsical conquest attitude, always eager to fight. In the episode that he's introduced, he is seen fighting with no weapons, during which he loses parts of two of his fingers. This doesn't bother him at all as he eccentrically keeps on fighting. Some episodes later, his group is shown bantering around Canute, the Christian prince. They make comments about how weak and soft Jesus looked on the cross. They comment about how easily Thorkell could knock Jesus out. As if this isn't enough, Canute is always presented with his face covered, as though in shame. When his face is ultimately revealed, he looks very feminine—with long blond hair, large blue eyes, and a soft voice. Canute starts off acting weak and pusillanimous, but as he grows, matures, becomes more confident, more assured, and more effective in his role, he becomes explicitly less Christian.[6] Although this is a Japanese production, it effectively illustrates how Christianity is commonly viewed as a religion that is both morally and physically weak and effeminate.

Understanding Men

The hormones testosterone and vasopressin exist in much greater quantity in males compared to females. According to an ex-psychotherapist and current attachment specialist Adam Lane Smith, vasopressin is a hormone that promotes deep bonds through stress and overcoming challenges. This means that men are sensitive to bonding through achieving goals, going through challenges, and helping others through their challenges. Testosterone is a hormone that makes men feel powerful and encourages them to reach the top of their domain. Simply put, men thrive in and feel good when they compete, win, and ultimately become an expert in their craft.[7]

This is why the classical school of thought believed that boys had to *grow* into men. Masculinity wasn't a birthright, but a prize claimed by those strong enough to lift the weight of the symbolic barbell. This was distinct from simply being male. It was the understanding that being a man was to understand your place in the larger social network. This is why throughout history many ancient and pre-modern societies had peculiar and seemingly brutal rituals for launching boys into manhood. They isolate men, force them to prove their strength and intellect, and then bring them back into society such that they can use their proven strength and intellect to lead society with the other men.

Another way boys grew into men was through war. War taught men physical strength, how to work as a unit, how to overcome their fears, and how to control their aggression. It taught them to root for and fight for their tribe, and in so doing to bond through a collective challenge. It made them want to become heroes, people who would be remembered by their peers or perhaps society, as heroes. War also required them to be intelligent so they could devise plans and understand complex military tactics.[8]

As I highlighted earlier in this book, sports plays a similar role in the life of boys, only in a much safer environment. You play on a team, you overcome obstacles, you root for your team, and you fight for your team, and if you win, you will be remembered and adored by your team and all of those who cheered for you. Michael Jordan and Wilt Chamberlain are celebrated basketball champions, and continuously seem to have an elusive mystique around them. They are seen as some kind of mythical legends who did amazing things in their legendary, bygone, vaguely understood era. This is not unlike how our generation reveres politicians such as Abraham Lincoln and war legends such as Ulysses S. Grant. This is why men with scars are seen as more attractive.[9] It is a badge of manhood. The implication is that they have gone through something difficult, like fighting a bear or tiger, and came out alive.

You may notice that I have previously spoken against doing things for self-aggrandizement, yet here I am promoting people who want to be acknowledged. This is because in order to be an effective leader, an acknowledgement of competence is a proven method to establish respect. And as a reminder, there is nothing wrong with wanting to be acknowledged as long as you understand that God and His righteous cause are more important, and ultimately greater than you, as explained in chapter 7.

What has become clear to me as I've researched Muscular Christianity is that to be a man is to demand something more of yourself. To achieve something great requires you to transform and go through a struggle. Part of the reason people like Kobe Bryant so much is that he worked so hard to get to where he did in basketball. Stories of Kobe's intense work ethic are legendary in the basketball community.

In *Wild At Heart*, John Eldridge states that in the heart of every man is a desperate desire for a battle to fight, an adventure to live, and a beauty to rescue.[10] This pithy list best describes what men are ordered towards. Men want to fight against something and ultimately win the competition. Men want to take risks on their journey toward something great. And men want women. The first two points require sacrificial excellence from men; however, modern Christianity doesn't seem to demand a lot from its adherents. I believe this is partly why it does not seem to attract the male population. There are no more fights to be won, no new frontiers to take. The culture has changed. Everything is relative. Competition has been minimized and discouraged. Our issues are now more emotional than physical. Our culture is now more individual than collective. Technology has taken the place of many physical activities that lend themselves to male fraternity.

Perhaps this is part of the reason Islam is more popular among men in America.[11] Islam shares many ethics with Christianity, including abstinence before marriage and steering away from pornography. But Islam emphasizes certain actions for all its followers, namely, the verbal proclamation of your faith, mandatory prayer five times every day, giving of alms, fasting during certain periods of the year, and making a pilgrimage to Mecca. Islam gives you something to do, and when you meet the challenge, you are considered a good Muslim. It calls on you to change and become a "better" person.

The sociological concept called "Credibility Enhancing Displays" states that people are more likely to believe a religious idea if they see someone acting as if that idea were true. This has been shown to be one of the best predictors of generational religiosity.[12] Living out your religion in demonstrable ways conveys to the people around you that you really do believe in your religion, which enhances the credibility of your message. Conversely, mere verbal expressions of belief provides limited efficacy.

Modern Christianity is intently focused on your relationship with God. Women are more relationship-oriented while men are more goal-oriented.[13] Christianity does call on you to change and strive to achieve goals, but this isn't highlighted in most denominations. People want to feel challenged; they want to think that their religion is serious, but that isn't emphasized enough in contemporary Christianity.

Christianity challenges you to be the best you can be and change your life in very substantive ways as people of God. Christianity wants you to use the skills and abilities God has given you to honor Him in your daily life. Christianity doesn't want to put shackles on your godly expression. Christianity affirms your inherent value, but it also calls on you to grow and become something better.

I think the message should be that you are fearful and wonderful in the way you were made, but God has called on you to improve on that base. What if changing yourself doesn't mean you have to give up who you are? What if it actually helps you realize who you are? What if it changes you into the ultimate version of yourself, fully manifesting the gifts God has given you? There is a highest form of yourself which exists that God has created you for. How exciting it is to make him manifest?

There are enough causes worthy of championing that should attract men into the Christian fold, but these are not emphasized. There are great sacrifices demanded from Christianity, but these are not emphasized. Men want to fight for something, to lead in a battle against something, to stive for greatness. To champion a cause greater than themselves while living a strenuous life. Contemporary Christianity is not providing these outlets.

The Two Sexes in Harmony

Christianity is neither a feminine nor a masculine religion. Christianity is the perfect harmony between the two sexes, synergizing into an ultimate blend of human excellence and perfection.

Men and women complement each other. According to John Gray's *Men are from Mars, Women are from Venus*, some traits come naturally to women and some to men. Some aspects of Christianity appeal to the feminine qualities of kindness, acceptance, and forgiveness, and some aspects of Christianity appeal to the masculine qualities of sacrifice, self-mastery, and competition—and this should be acknowledged.[14]

This isn't to say that men should ignore kindness, acceptance, and forgiveness, nor is it meant to suggest that women should ignore sacrifice, self-mastery, and competition. Most certainly this is not meant to say that a man who forgives is feminine; this is merely to say that these are the traits that come more naturally to the respective sexes. Additionally, men who have cultivated the quality of forgiveness, for example, will demonstrate it differently when compared to women. The same holds true for women and the masculine traits. There is a pure light of virtue that passes through a prism and refracts the colors of masculinity and femininity. Masculinity and femininity are like two instruments playing the same note. Even when they do the same thing, they sound different. Only when both the masculine and feminine are acknowledged and maximized, do we optimize human flourishing.

Christianity is set up so that it calls us to greatness on all fronts. Thus far, I have made it seem as if Western society is doing fine in the feminine area, but make no mistake, you cannot wither one sex without withering the other. The sexes are made for each other. Without a masculine influence, femininity will also face challenges. The fruits of their decline have a different yet similarly bitter flavor. But the church decline is primarily a male problem. The masculine side is in need of particular attention. I believe a way this can be accomplished is by getting Christian men more involved in sporting activities. I am not saying that sports can't be enjoyed by women, but there is no doubt that sports appeal more to male sensibilities because traits like physical aggression, self-mastery, and competition appeal more to men. So when I talk about those ideas, it is mainly men who it will resonate with it. It will be men who are on the frontlines of the battles that favor these traits being sharpened.

Manly Speaking...

I have been talking generally about Christianity throughout this book, but I want to focus on Christian men in this section. The ladies are equally important, of course, but the demographics for Christianity lean heavily in their favor, not to mention that the idea of muscularity, physical strength, and competition are ideals to which men have more natural affinity.

Plato uses the word *thumos* as an expression of male life energy through blood, sweat, and vigor.[15] It has to do with our will to fight and rebel against that which is intolerable. It is that fire in the belly that gives men the drive to defend their family, go for a workout in the blizzard, and be acknowledged as someone who is at the top of their craft.

Thumos is what drives entrepreneurs to take the risk in starting that company. *Thumos* is what the Spartan soldiers felt before heading into battle to defend their nation. *Thumos* is how we feel when we hit a bench press personal record.

These ideals are somewhat frowned upon in the contemporary Christian zeitgeist. Since Christianity is usually expressed through ways that have typically appealed to and associated with feminine nature, the male self is denied. Christ is always depicted as kind, loving, forgiving, and merciful—all of which are true; but all of which are also feminine-like characteristics. He is not often depicted as confrontational, leading, or competitive—character traits that are more natural to men. It feels as though men have to deny an intrinsic part of who they are in order to belong in modern-day Christianity.

There is no reason they have to feel this way. Changing the way you talk about the gospel around certain audiences is a completely valid tactic. 1 Corinthians 9:19–23 talks about how Paul varied his approach relative to the people to whom he was preaching in order to give himself the best chance at leading the various types of people to Christ. We don't need to change or twist Scripture in order to get more followers. We actually need to more closely adhere to what Scripture says to gain more followers. Please note that I am speaking generally here because all of us are born with a sinful nature and must continually deny that nature so we can be more like Christ. In this discussion, I am highlighting the fact that masculinity through the eyes of Christianity needs people approaching it.

The idea behind Muscular Christianity is to provide a safe and controlled outlet for high *thumos* men to express themselves. Professions such as firefighting, policing, and serving in armed forces have provided opportunities for *thumos*. The church, however, seems to be a place where *thumos* is unable to thrive. For one example, Theodore

Roosevelt was a Sunday school teacher before becoming president of the USA. One day, a boy showed up for class with a black eye admitting that he obtained this injury due to fighting another boy who was pinching his sister. Theodore told the boy that he was proud of him and gave him a dollar. When word got around, Roosevelt was duly fired.[16]

Muscular Christianity teaches the values of strength, courage, and endurance, and how they can be used to their proper end. These values are to be utilized to protect the weak and enable masculine, high *thumos* men to preach the Gospel and do their part to advance the kingdom of God.

In *Why Men Hate Going to Church* David Murrow explains how the metaphor of the bride and the bridegroom in the New Testament has been reinterpreted. In the original metaphor, Jesus was the bridegroom coming for the bride (the church); but in the modern interpretation, the bride is our individual soul. Over the years, we have replaced the glory of God with ourselves. We have made Jesus into someone whose ultimate goal is no longer to do the will of the Almighty God, but whose ultimate mission is to appease us.

Murrow cites Christian books with titles such as *Every Woman's Battle* and *When He Doesn't Believe* as books whose authors,

> vigorously encourage women to imagine Jesus as their personal lover. One tells her readers to "develop an affair with the one and only Lover who will truly satisfy your innermost desires: Jesus Christ. . . . This Someone entered your world and revealed to you that He is your true Husband. Then He dressed you in a wedding gown whiter than the whitest linen. You felt virginal again. And alive! He kissed

you with grace and vowed never to leave you or forsake you.
And you longed to go and be with Him.[17]

This is all to make the point that contemporary Christianity likes
to treat Jesus almost as an imaginary boyfriend to fulfill your desires,
and that imagery only really resonates with women. Where women are
more likely to take a liking to a sensitive and loving man, men look
more for someone to struggle and fight together with.

I have also observed that a lot of modern worship songs are basically love letters to Jesus, something that caters more to women. Indeed, most modern worship music could easily be contemporary love
songs if you substitute a few nouns. Men, on the other hand, are likely
to prefer traditional hymns. Those classical hymns were more likely to
cultivate an ethos of respect by acknowledging just how powerful and
holy God is, as opposed to focusing on His love and beauty. When I
was a child, I really liked the chorus of the song "Our God is an Awesome God." This was partly because every kid who grew up in the early
2000s had an obsession with the word "awesome," and partly because
the simple melody gave me visions of a great and mighty, conquering
God of the universe.

Both the all-powerful Deity who is *holy, holy, holy,* and the gentle
Father who will love you and care for you are important and accurate
depictions of God. God is a personal, loving, and beautiful deity with
endless mercy and grace. He is also powerful beyond our imagination
and holy beyond our comprehension. For the church to survive, all
these attributes must be preached and lived. Women have their role, so
do the men.

Perfection of Mind and Body

According to Plato, God gave men two ways to attain perfection: one through the mind and the other through the body, not separate, but together. Men will respect those who show mental intellect and wisdom as well as those who have physical strength. This is because it is through those faculties that people can control a given situation. They command respect. The tribe follows men who command respect and who can take control of all situations. This is why men take on leadership roles. These are the qualities that men want for themselves, the qualities that call others to follow them.

This is partly why I have so much reverence for Jesus and Paul in the Bible. Obviously, Jesus is the Son of God, and you could say I have a bias toward Paul because he is my namesake, but truly, they were men of wisdom and action fueled by indefatigable piety. They were wise because they always knew exactly what to say, and they gave amazing insight and wisdom on every issue. They were also men of action in that they did not care what consequences they would suffer for standing by the truth. Jesus was nailed to the cross for claiming He was the Son of God, and Paul was beheaded for promoting that claim. Jesus had all the power in the world, literally, and used it for the good of mankind. That is part of what makes Jesus's story so compelling. By all accounts, He was the most powerful man, but it was His willingness to confront the world and His virtue in using His power selflessly that I find most *awesome*.

The Manliest Man in Fiction

In the legendary best-selling manga series *One Piece*, a character named Edward Newgate (also known as Whitebeard) embodies the traits of the ideal man.[18] Whitebeard is introduced to the audience as the world's strongest man and captain of one of the four strongest pirate crews. He has incredible physical power and political influence. He was even best friends with the previous Pirate King, Gol. D. Roger. He uses this power to help the orphaned and to be a source of comfort to those in need. Whitebeard is an emblematic muscle man standing at twenty-one feet tall. But by the time we meet him, he is old and suffering from a life-threatening disease. He has one foot in the grave. Despite this, he gets up, suits up, and takes on the full force of the navy in his mission to retrieve a member of his pirate crew, all of whom he calls "family." Whitebeard fights for those he cares about even when he knows it will cost him his life. In the great war against the navy, Whitebeard never receives so much as a scratch on his back because he never turns back on those he fights for. Even when he dies, he stands tall and proud with his hand on his sword, firmly placed in the ground to keep his body upright. He dies standing up because even in death, his very will refuses to yield. Even in death, nothing in this world can make this man fall to his knees. In the manga panel where he dies, it reads,

> Even in death, even with half of his head blown clean away, his body refuses to yield. His mighty figure, cutting swathes through his foes, was truly monstrous. Over the course of his battles, he received a full two hundred and sixty-seven blade wounds. . . . The bullets he endured total one hundred and fifty-two. . . . And the cannonballs he has withstood amount to forty-six. And yet . . . Upon the proud back of this legendary man. . . . Or indeed, upon his very life as a pirate. . . . He bears not a single wound of cowardice![19]

While people rarely object to the idea that hyper aggressive *Fight Club* Tyler Durden type men are masculine, people will ultimately concede that people like Whitebeard are ultimately *more* masculine because they channel their masculine drive towards some good.

What Men Admire

Men don't admire passive or sedentary people. As we explained, men want an adventure to live by. In *Losing the Good Portion* Leon Poddles observes that "men are liable to lose respect for your traditional position when they lose respect for your muscles."[20]

Of course, big muscles aren't a prerequisite to being a leader, but they undoubtedly do help when trying to attract men to your cause. It conveys the fact, or at least the idea, that you are active and adventurous. Being fit gives a man a form of legitimacy to lead others as it clearly displays his commitment to duty and fighting through hardship instead of languishing in the pleasures of the world.

I do not believe *thumos* can be fully manifest without an incorporation of the spiritual life. What separates *thumos* from merely being high-testosterone male energy, is how *thumos* can be coupled with spirituality. *Thumos* is not a physiological reality like testosterone but a metaphysical reality. Prayer, meditation, and fasting are actions that reassert what it means to truly be human. It gives you an ultimate purpose, and when that purpose is manifest, it augments and steers that *thumos* onto the right path. Piety and *thumos* work in association, not contradiction. Muscular Christianity injects a potent virality-enhancing stimulant that enlivens the Christian man.

It is high-*thumos* men who will get married, make money, make babies, and build companies. Get young energetic men in the church, and we win the culture. I believe that to get these men back into the church, putting more emphasis on these masculine traits is worth considering. The contemporary church tells boys to be passive, to sheath their competitive drive, to never do anyone harm. But this is not helpful. We all have different gifts, proclivities, and affinities. Boys who are naturally more competitive need to cultivate that drive. Through doing so, or potentially after doing so, they will learn to control it by coupling it with meekness (or Aristotle's *praus*).

In times of peace, boys need a safe and proper outlet to release their natural urges and desires. Sports can be the crucial outlet they need to satisfy their urge to compete, their urge to attain mastery and wisdom, their desire for strength and control, as well as their natural aggressive tendencies.

Balance

Controlling that competitive spirit and drive is not an easy task. It is incomprehensibly difficult. Finding balance always is. Balance teaches the ability to use any ingredient necessary at a given time.

The goal should be balance and not moderation. Moderation implies you have a limited bottle that contains contradictory ingredients, never becoming more aggressive or more gentle than the bottle will allow, maintaining a mixture and equilibrium. Balance is more akin to a seesaw scale. You can tip the scale all the way in the aggressive direction at a given time, but you must also be able to tip it completely in the gentleness direction at a given time. One doesn't allow you to express something too much and the other allows you to express it totally, but you must also be able to express the opposing emotion in its fullness at any given time.

A way to demonstrate this is with a traumatic experience. Let's say someone faces trauma from a childhood experience. The due penalty should be put on to whomever committed the crime, and complete compassion should be shown to the victim. The scale turns both ways, and this equalizes and creates balance.

Murrow says, "Deep down, men long for a harsh affection—the love of a coach who yells at his players to get every ounce of effort; the love of a drill sergeant who pushes his recruits to the limits of human endurance; the love of a teacher who demands the impossible from his students. As Western society feminizes, it's getting harder for men to find this kind of love."[21]

This kind of relentless mindset has a few names. The two I am familiar with are "Mamba Mentality" named by the late Kobe Bryant, and "Killer Instinct," often associated with Michael Jordan. It is this idea that you ought to work as hard as you can, to the point where it is almost unreasonable. You feed the ruthlessness and tenacious urge to succeed and win.

In this pursuit, remember to stay humble, and recognize your place in the universe. You are strong, but you are still nowhere near God. There's a reason I emphasized the mind and body connection and specified the need for you to kneel down when praying. Kneeling is a submissive position. There is something incredibly striking about the juxtaposition of a strong man bowing before his Creator. Being strong connotes security, but kneeling down is the ultimate expression of vulnerability and submission. Kneeling before your Creator will help you remain humble. The mind, body, and spirit are connected, so when one kneels down in prayer, it communicates physically, mentally, and spiritually that you are weak. While no one wants to be seen as weak, that is precisely how you should feel in the presence of the Lord your God.

The Will of Divinity

One Piece, which I mentioned above, is a legendary story of a pirate by the name of Monkey D. Luffy, who sets out to sea to become the King of the Pirates. Along his long adventure, he recruits men of various talents to join his crew. The first member who joins is a swordsman by the name of Roronoa Zoro. Zoro is seen as a leader in his own right, oftentimes getting confused as the captain due to his sheer strength and conqueror's will. Zoro's dream is to become the world's greatest swordsman. Every moment he is not sleeping, he is training and fighting to achieve his goal. Throughout the narrative, we see just how determined he is to achieve that goal. He is stabbed, slashed, beaten, and bruised. But every time, he gets right back up stronger and more determined than before to pursue his dream. Every difficult battle is a reminder that he needs to become stronger. Zoro's drive is simply inhuman. Highlighted throughout the show is his willingness to be subservient to Luffy, which, shows how much more amazing his captain must be.

At the end of the "Thriller Bark" story arc, after a long battle, Luffy, along with almost everyone else, is knocked out. Though heavily injured, Zoro remains the only one awake. A new antagonist, Bartholomew Kuma, appears and attempts to kill Luffy, but Zoro fights back to protect his captain. Zoro soon realizes he stands no chance against Kuma and offers his life in place of Luffy's. Kuma agrees and supernaturally removes all of Luffy's pain and offers to transfer all of it to Zoro. To test his resolve, Kuma gives him a small dose, and it inflicts serious pain on him. Kuma tells Zoro that if he were to take all of it, especially in his current condition, he would die. Zoro, still resolute, and without a second thought, agrees to take in all of Luffy's pain. He nearly dies in the process. Kuma upholds his promise and leaves the island. Later, when people find Zoro standing in a sea of debris covered in blood, they ask him what happened. Zoro simply responds, "Nothing happened."[22]

Zoro's story reminds me of my own journey. Like Zoro, I am determined to reach my own goals. Yet I acknowledge that whatever aspirations I have are insignificant compared to the wonderful plans God has for me. I must be able to, at a moment's notice, give up everything I have, and more, for my God when He asks me to. To do this without complaining, boasting, or desiring to be seen as virtuous among men. To do this because of a genuine desire to serve my Lord above anything else, is my constant prayer.

A Foreign Christianity

How I'm describing Christianity may be foreign to you. It might even sound like a different religion entirely. Part of this is due to the outright secularization of the church. Many people don't even know what authentic Christianity is anymore. A lot of the messages you hear from church pulpits are indistinguishable from those you hear from the secular world. Churches often look, sound, and in every way resemble the rest of the culture, seeming to be products of the secular world as opposed to windows into something eternal, sacred, and supernatural. In a bid to seem more approachable and to not upset or scare anyone, churches secularize their message. But this ultimately dilutes the faith and bores their congregations while not attracting outsiders.

Another reason that you may not have heard Christianity spoken of like this is because of the way most churches frame our ultimate purpose. As Murrow points out, the gospel has changed over the years. "In today's church, the gospel is no longer about saving the world against impossible odds. It's about finding a happy relationship with a wonderful man."[23]

The Church's reluctance to challenge people, to go on a wild adventure, to build a kingdom, and fight the forces of hell ultimately bores men. Think of every story popular among boys. It involves saving the world against overwhelming adversity and never giving up in the face of unspeakably stacked odds. Boys' stories are found in superhero comics, *Shonen* manga, spy fiction, being down 3–1 in the NBA finals, and making that epic comeback in the World Cup finals. This is because deep inside ourselves we all want to be heroes, and we project ourselves onto those stories.

What makes these stories so intriguing, why they are passed on from generation to generation, and why a lot of religions tell them, is their ability to capture the essence of humanity. They distill, communicate, and clarify it; they bring to focus what we are and what we ought to be. For men, the stories that inspire them are ones where they become their ideal, superhero self.

We may think that imitation is for children, and perhaps some of the superficial imitation is, but I think that imitation is a human trait we all possess. The media and the television shows we consume influence and motivate us. Zoro from *One Piece* motivates me. These capacities and behaviors lie dormant within our nature and can be unleashed with a potent enough stimulus. These stories can motivate us in ways that cannot be fully articulated, and to a degree far greater than we could have if we tried to reason it out. Exemplars of virtue move us more than the ethical maxims of philosophy. Values resonate more with us through stories that we can intimately attach ourselves to.

Now consider the following story: A prophesied boy is born into this world with his greatest war enemy eagerly waiting to kill him upon birth. He is assigned the impossible task of changing the world and overcoming a powerful enemy. For much of his life he is undercover, but later he recruits a few allies. One of those allies betrays him for some flimsy reward, and he is handed to the enemy and is beaten to death. Despite all of this, he miraculously revives, escapes the enemy, and wins in the most epic fashion.

What story is this? Naruto? Superman? Aang from *Avatar: The Last Airbender*? I wouldn't blame you for thinking that, but the story is actually the one told in the Bible about Jesus Christ. It's set up like any other epic story. The difference is, we are living out this epic story. Jesus's story is one we are a part of. Jesus asks us to set aside everything and follow Him, inviting us to join Him on His quest to flip the world on its head. It is one where we overcome the very concept of evil itself. What could possibly be more epic than that? We are at battle with evil, and with God by our side, we will experience absolute victory. If God is for us, who can stand against us? Satan is seething, knowing full well that he will lose but resisting all the same. We already have the story spoiled for us. We know the ending. Satan will be crushed. God will wipe every tear from our eye, and there will be no more pain or death. Satan loses. God wins. He rules the earth with His iron scepter. Simply reframing the story gives an entirely different perspective.[24]

Walk into many churches and you will rarely hear about struggle, about pain, about sacrifice. Instead, you will hear about finding a personal relationship with God. There is no heroism, no epic fight, no great battle, no conflict that might energize and create pious men to fight and take action. If we pointed a light on that side of Christianity, it could perhaps light a fire in people who didn't even know they had that flame to begin with.

We are fighting for truth. Once the truth is known, the fire is lit, and you can't extinguish it. It sets your heart ablaze. The Bible is full of people who died for the truth, gave up their bodies to protect it. Their sacrifices will not go unnoticed. We take up the cross and are beaten, whipped, and spat on by the world. But in due time, the burden becomes light, and the yoke is made easy. The truth will win, and all of those who fought for it will be rewarded with their names written indelibly in the Book of Life and told a job well done by the righteous God.

This focus on our personal relationship with Jesus makes the Christian faith a private matter. But manhood dictates that you prove yourself in the public sphere and create a legacy that endures generations. This is perhaps why we see a growing trend of people becoming spiritual and not religious. Similarly, some Christians say that Christianity isn't a religion but a relationship. Religion is an objectively measured practice. Spirituality is primarily an individual feeling. Self-described spiritual people enjoy the feeling of being connected to something higher and being drawn to a greater purpose, but they don't want to sacrifice anything, which is usually required by most religions. A private practice, by its very nature, cannot endure generations into the future, nor can it impact the community at large. If your relationship with God is purely personal, attending church becomes optional, singing and praising are completely out of the question. And this "personal relationship" thing is never actually mentioned in the Bible.

I do agree that our relationship with God is profoundly personal. There is a deeply true sentiment behind the personal relationship mantra, but it is important to acknowledge that Christianity is also a faith you live out publicly. When a religion is made public, it stands out. When faith is shared, it makes everyone's faith stronger—and gives it credibility. We see that person and think they are different from the rest. But many Christian's lives are indistinguishable from their secular counterparts. So while the personal relationship idea speaks to a certain truth, in my experience it has often been used as an excuse to cajole Christians into not acting like the Christians they know they ought to be.

The Fight

Running, lifting weights, or playing sports isn't anywhere as difficult or honorable as serving God. But it is a catalyst that can help us cultivate that mentality to take up more glorious tasks. It teaches us how to fight and work for results, it teaches us how to persevere. We may not be warriors going to the battlefield, but that warrior's spirit still lives in us. This drive should be harnessed, not contained. A lack of men in the pews directly results in fewer Christians, which directly results in societal entropy. God made us this way for a reason. It is the men of the society who will be on the front lines in this unapologetic fight to reignite the Christian soul of Western civilization. This will be a challenging fight. An adventurous fight. The closest analog to that warrior's drive in modern times is sports. We work with a team, with a coach, or with a gym partner, someone who will keep pushing us to go beyond our limits. We learn how to cooperate. We struggle together and rise together. We learn how to fight, to give hits, and to receive them.

Unlike in actual war, through sports, we can express and cultivate these values in a safe environment. No lives are lost. In fact what happens is the reverse. We take care of our bodies and keep God's creation in its best condition for the fight. We have this amazing gift of the body that we can use to vitalize the soul. A full understanding of the body will turn our men into the type of people best equipped to win this fight. That is why sports are so important, why athletics are important. That is why taking care of your body is so important, why maximizing your physical prowess is important.

In athletics, you understand the sweet bliss of victory, the agony of loss, and the necessity of certain virtues. Through athletics we can cultivate the virtues Christianity so desperately needs to focus on right now—the virtues that will primarily be mastered by men. That is why we need Muscular Christianity.

Part IV:
Practical
Advice

CHAPTER 15

Practical Advice

———————————=✕( )✕=———————————

No man has the right to be an amateur in the matter of physical training.
It is a shame for a man to grow old without seeing the
beauty and strength of which his body is capable.

–Socrates

Did You Know?

On average, we spend nine hours at school or work and eight hours sleeping every day. That leaves seven hours for other things like eating and exercising. Ninety percent of your inability to work out is less about time availability and more about priority-setting because you can get a good workout in forty-five minutes. If you exercise three times a week for forty-five minutes, that's two hours and fifteen minutes a week. That's 1.3 percent of your week.

From my experience this is all you really need to stay in decent shape and receive the bulk of the benefits of exercising. But because forty-five minutes three times a week doesn't seem like much, you may be tempted to delay exercising until the next day. We procrastinate and tell ourselves, "I'll do it tomorrow." But "what we needlessly put off until the next day most likely will never happen because tomorrow will in all probability be very much like today"[1] according to Dr. Christopher Kaczor in *The Gospel of Happiness*. It is better to do what you need to do today and leave tomorrow an open question than delay what you need to do today and hope tomorrow is different.

Throughout this book, I have talked about the importance of exercise. Every form of exercise has its own unique benefits. Here are some examples:

- Exercise can help your brain function and manage anxiety. This is best done through moderate aerobic exercises like jump rope, jogging, and any sport where you run for a long time.

- Exercise can help curb addiction. This is best done through organized team sports.

- Exercise can help slow the process of aging. This is best done through resistance training.

- Exercise can increase focus. Sports that require a lot of spatial complexity like gymnastics, martial arts, parkour, and skateboarding have been known to help.

Types of Strength

Psychologists have identified seven types of strength:

1. Maximal Strength
2. Relative Strength
3. Explosive Strength
4. Endurance Strength
5. Agile Strength
6. Speed Strength
7. Starting Strength

We will be looking at the first four in this section, starting with definitions.

1. *Maximal strength* refers to your raw strength—how much weight you can lift, your maximum bench press, your squat, and your deadlift. You see maximal strength in people who compete in strongman competitions, linemen in the NFL, or rugby players. Typically, these people will be on the bulky side.

2. ***Relative strength*** describes how strong you are relative to your bodyweight. This is your ability to lift many times more than your body weight. This is the power of calisthenics athletes, rock climbers, gymnasts, and lightweight powerlifters. If absolute strength could help you lift a car, relative strength helps you climb a tree or climb up a ledge. It is important for you to be able to move your own body weight; that way, you can stay mobile and agile.

3. ***Explosive strength*** is your ability to generate power. Power refers to your burst of energy. This is how fast you can reach top speed when running, how high you can jump and how hard you can punch. This is the power you see in track and field and boxing.

4. ***Endurance strength*** is how well you can exert a force over a long period of time. This includes your cardiovascular endurance as well as muscular endurance. Examples of muscular endurance are long-distance running, swimming, and cycling.

Everyone has different strengths. Some people will have great maximal and relative strength, whereas some other people may have good endurance strength. They are all important for different situations. I think it is important to work on all these areas to become a well-rounded athlete. When it comes to exercises, I think it is better to be a jack of all trades than a master of one. Have a good base of strength in all areas, and then choose one of them that you want to specialize in. You don't have to specialize, but I find that it is more rewarding and guarantees long term adherence when you work on things you are good at.

Personally, I have five pillars of athleticism that I work on:

1. Strength (maximal and relative strength)

2. Speed (explosive strength)
3. Endurance (endurance strength)
4. Flexibility
5. Coordination

Training the four strengths I described above will help to achieve these five pillars of athleticism. These pillars can be achieved by engaging in almost any combination of two sports. Some sports individually probably hit all five.

One question I always got growing up was why I never took up martial arts. I enjoy anime, which takes heavy inspiration from that field, and it seems like something that would follow my philosophy. For me it's similar to football. I enjoyed playing the sport recreationally in my adolescence and have respect for the strong and fast athletes that partake in it. However, I have no desire to partake in those sports at a high level. For me, these sports are too rough. Martial arts such as MMA and Boxing are amazing for personal exercise, self-discipline, and self-defense. They hit all my five pillars of athleticism. But to play it at a high level is to risk all sorts of major and serious injuries. It's the same reason I don't play football. People don't typically die in football or sustain life-altering concussions, but they do sustain minor concussions over time from bonking their heads so often. Researchers have proved that this can have deleterious effects on the athletes as explained in chapter 10. I don't want those things to happen to me. Therefore, my focus in high school was basketball, and my focus in university was calisthenics. I plan on taking up martial arts recreationally someday, but not at a competitive level. I cast no judgment on those who participate in them competitively; I just personally won't.

Along with fighting, I also believe gymnastics mixes all my five pillars. I don't think there is a sport out there that creates a more complete

athlete than gymnastics. So, if you were to ask me which sport emphasizes all these pillars the most effectively, I would choose gymnastics,
with various martial arts being a close second.

This was my very brief guide to steer you in the direction of physical fitness. On the following pages, I will give you advice specifically
for bodybuilding since that is where I am most knowledgeable.

Effective Bodybuilding

Workout Frequency

Work out your body parts at least two times a week. Training the
muscle group more frequently than that may be acceptable if you are
advanced or if you didn't train the muscle group with a lot of volume
in the previous days.

How Hard Should You Train?

How hard you should train is a hot topic in the fitness industry.
Fitness influencers like Greg Doucette say we should train harder than
last time, but other influencers like Jeff Nippard say we should be more
moderate in our training and leave some reps in the tank.

My approach is somewhere in the middle. I think that there is wisdom in training a little harder every time, whether that be doing one
more rep, doing some reps slower, doing the same number of reps with
cleaner form, doing the same number of reps with higher weight, or
shorter rest times.

One of the problems that arises from this question is that most people have no idea how hard they can actually push. A study assessed 160
men and found that most people highly underestimate how many reps
they can do on a given exercise. The researchers asked the participants,
"What is a typical weight you would use for 10 reps?" This was not

asking how many reps they thought they could do if they went all out, but merely asking how many they usually worked with. The researchers then took them to the gym and tested how many they could actually do when pushed to failure. They found that on average, people were able to do sixteen reps.[2]

This means that on average, people stop six reps shy of failure, which does not optimize muscle hypertrophy. It is my belief that for compound movements, your working sets should be about two-to-three reps shy of failure. For isolation movements they should be one-to-two reps shy of failure. This notwithstanding, I believe that you should do as many reps as you can on the last working set. In other words, train to absolute failure on your last set of a muscle group that you are working. Additionally, some days you should go as hard as you can in a single set early in the workout so that you have a benchmark for just how hard you can push yourself on a given exercise. You will never know how close you are to training to failure unless you actually train to failure. Occasionally training to failure is a good way to gauge of how far you can push on an exercise.

There's also the question of what failure actually means. Does it mean you can't do a rep with good form anymore, as in mechanical failure? Does it mean you can't do a rep with bad form anymore? Or that you can't move your muscle on the machine/bar/bodyweight movement at all, as in muscular failure?

I think it depends on the exercise. For big compound movements, failure should mean mechanical failure. Doing a sloppy squat rep can be dangerous. When it comes to isolation movements, I do them until I am unable to even complete a half rep, around one or two reps shy of muscular failure. If you exercise on machines, you can probably go even further beyond and push past muscular failure with the aid of negatives. For example, on the leg extension you can use both legs to lift the weight up, and then use one leg to control the weight down.

As for how hard you personally should be training, I think you need to ask yourself two questions.

1. How much do I *really* want to improve?
2. How experienced am I?

For the first question, I don't just say this as an act of formality like these trainers tend to, I mean do you *really* want to push yourself as hard as you possibly can? Do you want to get the *best* results possible? You will physically and mentally exhaust yourself if you do, but you will maximize your growth response.

If the answer is that you want to get better but not push so hard that you use up too much energy and physical resources, then you should train moderately hard. Maybe you have a day job where you do a lot of manual labor. Maybe you have other responsibilities, and you think they will be impeded by going too hard in the gym. Maybe you just want to lose some fat but not gain muscle. Maybe this is all a fun hobby to you and any extra muscle is just a bonus, a byproduct, something that is nice to have. That is fine. The gym will still improve your mental and physical health, keeping your mind, bones, and brain sharp. If you want the best results possible, you will have to train as hard as you can within the parameters I established previously. When I say train to failure, I mean you get to the point that even if you were offered a million dollars to do another rep, you physically couldn't.

As for the second question, if you are a beginner, you should be training lightly. Conversely, if you are experienced, you should be training hard. Beginners could almost play around with the weights and get used to the form for the first couple months and still grow. They will likely even get sore just from this. Their muscles aren't used to being pushed like that, so they are also at a high risk of injury if they go too hard. As they become stronger, they can train harder and longer until they become advanced and are able to comfortably train hard.

Taking both of those together, you should only be training hard if you want maximum results and are experienced.

Repetition (Rep) Range

Many people swear by the six-to-twelve rep range for ideal gains, but in my experience, the number of rep ranges doesn't really matter as long as it's over five and under thirty.

The problem with super low reps, under five reps, is that they don't cause enough muscle tear; so you will be gaining mostly strength and not muscle. You will be teaching your brain and muscles to exert as much power as possible in one swoop. That doesn't optimally build muscle. This rep range also leaves you more susceptible to injury.

On the other hand, doing reps above thirty takes far too much time and requires too much rest in between, which will inhibit the amount of muscle damage you will incur. This is because you should be resting for about three-to-six minutes between sets and that isn't enough time to rest when you are approximating failure for such a long period of time. It is also mentally taxing and hard on your cardiovascular endurance. So practically speaking, in my experience the best rep range is seven-to-fifteen for most exercises for the vast majority of people, closer to fifteen for the isolation exercises and closer to seven for the compound movements.

How Long Should You Rest?

How long I rest depends on the exercise. For heavy compound movements I will rest for five-to-six minutes, and for single joint movements I rest for one-to-three minutes.

Workout Splits

Push Day: a push day refers to a specific workout session where you focus on exercises that involve pushing movements. These exercises primarily target your chest, shoulders, and tricep muscles.

Pull Day: a pull day refers to a specific workout session where you focus on exercises that involve pulling movements. These exercises primarily target your back, biceps, and rear shoulder muscles.

Leg Day: a leg day is a workout session where you focus on exercises that primarily target your leg muscles. This includes your quadriceps (front of the thighs), hamstrings (back of the thighs), glutes (buttocks), and calves.

Upper Day: an upper body day is a workout session where you focus on exercises that target the upper body muscles. The muscles worked include all of the muscles mentioned in the push and pull days.

Lower Day: another term for leg day. Lower day is usually used to better coordinate with an "upper day" if you are running an upper/lower training split.

Full body: A full body workout refers to a single workout session that incorporates all or most muscle groups.

I like to alternate muscle groups and exercise patterns. If I have a pull day, I will do weighted pullups to start, and then do bicep curls after, then do rows, and then do a different variation of bicep curls. One movement focuses more on pulling yourself up with back muscles while using the biceps as support, the next is a focused bicep movement, the next is a back movement, and the next is another bicep movement. It helps my muscles stay warm and also get a bit of rest so they can perform optimally for the next exercise. I find that doing the barbell bench press and immediately following it with a dumbbell bench press over-fatigues my muscles. But when I do a shoulder press instead of dumbbell bench press, I can function better by giving my chest a break before I get into the dumbbell bench press.

You can change up the movement pattern even if you are still working on the same muscle group. If you do a bench press, you can do a chest fly after, and since it is hitting your muscles in a different way, it can still work, even though it is still working the same muscle group. I just don't do the barbell bench press and then immediately go into the dumbbell bench press.

In terms of how I split my muscle groups, I like to do a push-pull leg split, but I think an upper-lower split and full-body workout split work perfectly fine as well. I feel a strong compulsion to go to the gym as often as possible, so I go five-to-six days a week, but that may not fit your schedule. I think your split generally comes down to your own preference. Just keep in mind my previous recommendation of training a muscle group two times a week.

Exercise Variation

There has also been a debate on just how many exercises you need per muscle group. On one hand we have minimalists who do five or six fundamental exercises and claim that is enough to train their entire body, and on the other hand we have people who do twenty variations of the bench press. I lie somewhere in between because I do general exercises for the muscles I want to maintain, and I do specific exercises for the muscles I want to focus on. I will probably never do more than six different exercises for a muscle group because anything after that would be too hard to keep track of, too fatiguing, and could end up being redundant. Your physiology is not so sensitive as to need twenty-five different exercises for each muscle hitting each individual fiber in slightly different ways. My advice to you is to find the three or four exercises per muscle group that you enjoy and focus on them. Those exercises should cover all the main functions of the muscle group.

As I previously explained, there are many ways to work out. Some people like a cardio focus, some do yoga, some play individual sports, some play team sports, some like martial arts, some like to powerlift, and some like to bodybuild. I try to do a mix of all of them with a primary focus on bodybuilding. I recommend that you try and experience at least two of these. I think we should be able to move our bodies the best way we can, staying flexible, staying strong, and having functional muscles. This is why I incorporate calisthenics (bodyweight exercises) to my routine.

To be fully functional as an athlete, you need to be able to lift yourself and lift the objects around you. "Functional" is a very vague buzzword. I think "nature training" is more accurate because this training adheres to the ways our bodies are naturally designed. The fact that calisthenics works on the pillars I mentioned earlier, and has a higher correlation with weight strength than weight strength has with calisthenics, makes me believe they are more natural movements. Put more simply, someone who can do handstand push-ups will have a good overhead press, but there is a far weaker correlation between someone with a strong overhead press and a good handstand push up. I think that unless you are a professional athlete, or striving to be one, you should incorporate a mix of workouts to your routine.

Notice throughout the book that I used a lot of metaphors and examples from all different disciplines of fitness. This isn't because I want to seem quirky and inclusive, but it is because they all offer something unique to the formation of human character, and it is important to understand all of them.

There is some merit in being both functional and aesthetic. Austin Dunham's philosophy when it comes to building muscle is to be a "bodyweight bodybuilder." This is someone who uses bodyweight movements to build muscle, applying a bodybuilder's mentality of focusing on sets and reps, progressive overload, and diet. Fitness influencer Austin Dunham has been described as a large and aesthetic man who uses his muscles in unexpected and dynamic ways. Bioneer, another influencer, has similarly coined this mixture "Functional Aesthetics."[3]

When Should You Work out?

For self-improvement purposes, I think it is best to work out in the mornings. That way you get energized right as you wake up and it also helps you to sleep early. In *Art of the Impossible*, Steven Kotler summarizes research conducted by the psychologist Roy Baumeister demonstrating that willpower peaks in the morning.[4] So if you have trouble getting yourself to work out at the end of a long day of work, this may be something worth considering. However, to maximize the effectiveness of the workout, it is probably better to work out in the afternoon or evening because at that point your muscles and hormones have properly warmed up. The choice is entirely yours. There isn't a major difference either way.

Bulk or Cut?

Bulk: A bulk refers to a phase of a diet and training program aimed at increasing muscle mass and overall body weight. The goal during a bulk is to consume a caloric surplus, which means consuming more calories than you burn, in order to provide the necessary energy and nutrients for muscle growth.

Cut: a cut refers to a phase of a diet and training program aimed at reducing body fat while preserving muscle mass. The goal during a cut is to consume a calorie deficit, which means consuming less calories than you burn. The primary goal during a cut is to lose fat while preserving as much muscle as possible.

Contrary to popular belief, you don't actually need to bulk and cut to get stronger. This isn't to say that bulking and cutting is useless, but it is to say that this talk of only being able to build muscle in a calorie surplus is probably exaggerated.

I am not saying that you can eat the same way every day and perpetually continue to gain muscle. Your muscles at some point will need more food to grow, so you will find there to be a time when you will need to eat more than you are used to in order to gain muscle. Some degree of bulking and cutting is likely necessary as you reach more advanced levels of exercise. If you find that you are plateauing at the gym, I recommend bulking up a bit. But becoming a gelatinous ball of fat and force-feeding yourself only to shed it off in hopes that you can magically retain a significant amount of that size, only now in the form of muscle, is probably not necessary.

Genetics and Potential

Now let's talk genetics. Whether we want to believe it or not, *genetics matter*. People have different genetic potentials. I have always excelled in power sports like sprinting and basketball, and I build muscle easily. I have fast twitch muscles, so it is likely that I have very sensitive androgen receptors, and some degree of myostatin deficiency. I have no control over that. Even before I started working out, I looked physically better than a lot of people who were already months into their workout routine. Bodybuilding is one of those things that is so highly genetic that you are wasting your time envying those you cannot compete with. (Remember that in the Bible, envy is a sin!) Some people are built differently and will respond to training more or less than others. It's not fair. Unfortunately, that's life.

Skinny people are skinny often because they naturally have a propensity to be so, and muscular people are big and become exponentially more big after working out because they are genetically inclined that way. That is reality. However, unlike the famous economic mantra—the rich get richer, and the poor get poorer—the rich will get richer, but the poor can still make some good progress. Unfavorable genetics isn't an excuse to not exercise.

What is great about athletics is that there is always something for everyone. If you are bad at one sport or genetically ill-suited for it, there is a sport out there that emphasizes the polar opposite traits in which you will likely find more success. The physical mechanisms and genetic patterns favorable to gaining muscles are antithetical to those for running long distances. You may find more success there. But it is still great if you want to build muscle.

A word of encouragement for everyone who isn't especially inclined to one specific sport: Don't give up because of your genetic makeup.

As cheesy as it sounds, I encourage you to compare yourself to yourself. You may certainly admire those elite specimens for the amazing bodies God has given them, but at the end of the day, you should be comparing yourself to yourself. What lies within their capacities may not lie within yours.

There are some hyper responders who start off skinny and gain a lot of muscle, such as Russell Orhii, but from my observation those are the exceptions, not the rule. The reason we think they are the rule is because when it does happen, it is so shocking and we all pay attention to it. Seeing someone go from skinny to buff is a lot more shocking than seeing someone go from fit to fitter.

Calisthenics VS Weights

Around 2016 there was a massive debate in the fitness industry about the effectiveness of calisthenics and how it compares to lifting weights. My advice on the issue is very simple: Do both. Calisthenics provides a safer, beginner-friendly, and cheap form of exercise. It also looks cool and works on your balance, coordination, and flexibility. There's a particular kind of strength you gain that makes calisthenics extremely rewarding. Not everyone can comprehend and acknowledge just how impressive a 405 lb bench press is, but anyone can understand and acknowledge how impressive a handstand push-up is.

The shortcomings of calisthenics lie in the fact that progression is usually limited by skill acquisition, not strength. There isn't a linear progression between the exercises. There is a big jump between pike push-ups and handstand push-ups, but there isn't as big of a jump between a 150 lb overhead press and a 160 lb overhead press. Calisthenics is also bad at isolating muscles. This can make your physique look unbalanced and it can be harder to work around injuries.

Weights are easier to progress with, easier to learn, and allow you to specialize more easily. Which one you decide to focus on is up to you, but I strongly suggest you do both.

It is very common to find bikers with overdeveloped legs or wrestlers with over-developed traps or calisthenics athletes/gymnasts who have under-developed legs. It could be unhealthy to have oversized muscle groups, so it is probably in their best interest, health-wise, to bring up the other muscles.

Bodybuilding and having an aesthetic physique can mitigate these muscle imbalances.

Upauli's Workout Routine

Up until now, I have shared with you my general workout philosophy. I will now describe to you my specific workout plan. These are what work for me. I hope you can learn from them. But if you are getting results with another method that you find more comfortable, then prioritize that. It is more important that you are exercising in general than following my specific routine. These are merely my suggestions drawing from my own research and experience. If you would like to modify it to better represent your own desires and preferences, be my guest.

The routine I will share with you is one I used to gain the majority of my muscle. The physique you see in my photos at the beginning of each part of the book were developed through the use of this routine. This is what I did from about month six to year two of training. I have made alterations through the years due to changes in my current lifestyle and changes to my training knowledge bank. What alterations might those be, you ask? That's something best saved for another workout plan I may sell through my YouTube channel.

During the time I was using this workout program, building my biceps was a top priority, so you can see that there is a lot of volume dedicated to that muscle group. Generally speaking, I train with a lot of volume because in my experience, increasing that variable has been shown to be the best way for me to make long term gains. People are often shocked at how much volume I do. But studies have also backed up my experience. Brad Schoenfeld and others looked at men with one year or more of training experience and put them through different workout programs. A dose-dependent relationship was found. The more sets they did, the more hypertrophy they accumulated. Those who did five sets on seven exercises in a workout saw the best results.

Some participants did up to forty-five sets of legs per week, and they saw the best results.[5] I did not program doing forty-five sets of any muscle group. I have my doubts about this being sustainable for long term gains. I have tried it before and got injured, but even if you can stay injury free, I believe that this will probably lead to overtraining. Regardless, it does show strong evidence for more sets being highly beneficial to experienced lifters.

I give a rep range for each set because you likely won't be able to get the same number of reps each set. I have also provided a more beginner-friendly workout routine for those who want to build muscle but don't have time to go to the gym six days a week or for people who are beginners.

Points to Note about My Workouts

Unless specified, I do all exercises for seven-to-ten reps.

- I take a rest between sets—three-to-six minutes, depending on the exercise.

- I don't worry if I can't do all the exercises in one day or get too tired. I just do as much as I can. I don't worry if I miss a day or two; I just come back the next day.

- "OR" implies a different variation, whereas a slash (/) implies an easier variation if you aren't able to perform it.

Six-Day Split

Monday: Horizontal Push

3 sets: Weighted Dips/Bodyweight Dips/Assisted Dips

OR

3 sets: Dumbbell Chest Press

OR

3 sets: Barbell Bench Press

----

3 sets: Dumbbell Shoulder Press

OR

3 sets: Overhead Press

----

3 sets: Incline Dumbbell Press

3 sets: Lateral Raises

3 sets: Tricep Push-downs

3 sets: Bodyweight Dips (skip if you did regular dips before)

(OPTIONAL)

1 minute of Forearm Twists

Tuesday: Vertical Pulling (Bicep Focus)

3 sets: Weighted Pull-ups/Bodyweight Pull-ups/Lat Pull-down

3 sets: Barbell Bicep Curl

3 sets: Front-lever Raises/Straight-arm Pull-down

3 sets: Preacher Curls

3 sets: Machine Row

1 set: Bodyweight Chin-ups AMRAP (as many reps as possible)

(OPTIONAL) 3 sets: Face Pulls/Reverse Chest Fly

Wednesday: Legs Focus
5 sets: Barbell Squats 5–7 reps
3 sets: Leg Press
3 sets: Weighted Lunges
3 sets: Weighted Single Leg Glute Bridge
3 sets: Seated Calf Raises

Thursday: Vertical Push
(I only do these If I have my gymnastics rings. If I don't, I repeat Monday with the alternate exercises)
3 sets: Archer Dips
OR
3 sets: Weighted Dips

----

3 sets: Chest Fly
3 sets: Ring Dips
2 sets: Tricep Extension
3 sets: Ring Rear Delt Raise
2 sets: Ring Push-ups

Friday: Horizontal Pulling (Back Focus)
5 sets: Front Lever Raises/Straight-arm Pull-down

----

3 sets: Barbell Bicep Curl
OR
3 sets: Preacher Curl

(skip if you can't do it)
3 sets: Front Lever Pullup Progression
OR

3 sets: Ice Cream Maker

----

4 sets: Hammer Curl w/Slow Eccentric
3 sets: Bodyweight Rows/Bent-over Barbell Rows
1 set: Dead Hang as long as possible

Saturday: Legs
4 sets: Trap Bar Deadlift
3 sets: Glute Ham Raise
3 sets: Hamstring Curl

Sunday: Rest
On Sundays, I practice advanced calisthenics skills (like handstands)
and stretch if I feel up to it. Otherwise I rest.

UPAULI'S WORKOUT ROUTINE

MONDAY

	SETSXREPS
BENCH PRESS	3X7-10
OVERHEAD PRESS	3X7-10
INCLINE DUMBBELL PRESS	3X7-10
LATERAL RAISES	3X7-10
TRICEP PUSHDOWN	3X7-10
DIPS	3X7-10
OPTIONAL FOREARM BARBELL TWIST	1 MIN

TUESDAY

	SETSXREPS
PULL UPS	3X7-10
BARBELL BICEP CURL	3X7-10
FRONT LEVER RAISE	3X7-10
PREACHER CURL	
MACHINE ROWS	3X7-10
CHIN UP	3X7-10
OPTIONAL FACE PULLS	3X7-10

WEDNESDAY

	SETSXREPS
SQUATS	5X5-7
LEG PRESS	3X7-10
WEIGHTED LUNGES	3X7-10
SINGLE LEG GLUTE BRIDGE	3X7-10
SEATED CALF RAISES	3X7-10

THURSDAY

	SETSXREPS
ARCHER DIPS	3X7-10
RING CHEST FLY	3X7-10
RING DIPS	3X7-10
RING TRICEP EXTENTION	2X7-10
RING REAR DELT RAISES	3X7-10
RING PUSH UPS	2X7-10

FRIDAY

	SETSXREPS
STRAIGHT ARM PULLDOWN	3X7-10
BARBELL BICEP CURL	3X7-10
FRONT LEVER ROW	3X7-10
HAMMER CURL	3X7-10
BODYWEIGHT ROWS	4X7-10
OPTIONAL DEAD HANG	1X∞

SATURDAY

	SETSXREPS
TRAP BAR DEADLIFT	4X7-10
GLUTE HAM RAISE	3X7-10
HAMSTRING CURL	3X7-10

SUNDAY IS A REST DAY

Three-Day Split

Day 1:
3 sets: Incline Bench Press
3 sets: Pull-ups
3 sets: Leg Press
3 sets: Machine Rows
3 sets: Dips

Day 2:
3 sets: Pull-ups
3 sets: Dumbbell Bench Press
3 sets: Wide Grip Machine Rows
3 sets: Overhead Tricep Extension
3 sets: Bicep Curl
3 sets: Lateral Raise

Day 3:
3 sets: Squats
3 sets: Reverse Lunges
3 sets: Leg Extension
3 sets: Ab Rollout

UPAULI'S WORKOUT ROUTINE

DAY 1	SETSXREPS
INCLINE BENCH PRESS	3X7-10
PULL UPS	3X7-10
LEG PRESS	3X7-10
MACHINE ROWS	3X10-15
DIPS	3X10-15

DAY 2	SETSXREPS
PULL UPS	3X7-10
DUMBBELL BENCH PRESS	3X7-10
WIDE GRIP MACHINE ROWS	3X7-10
OVERHEAD TRICEP EXTENTION	3X7-10
BICEP CURLS	3X7-10
LATERAL RAISE	3X7-10

DAY 3	SETSXREPS
SQUATS	3X7-10
REVERSE LUNGES	3X7-10
LEG EXTENTIONS	3X7-10
AB ROLLOUT	3X7-10

Exercise Tutorials

Subscribe to my general YouTube channel: https://www.youtube.com/c/DrUpauli

Subscribe to my fitness YouTube channel: https://www.youtube.com/c/UpauliAthletics

Follow my Instagram page: https://www.instagram.com/upauli_athletics/

Follow my fitness TikTok account: https://www.tiktok.com/@upauliathletics

Email for business inquiries: upaulienterprise@gmail.com

Notes

Preface

1. "Muscular Christianity," Wikipedia, May 4, 2023, https://en.wikipedia.org/wiki/Muscular_Christianity
2. My YouTube channel *DrUpauli,* https://www.youtube.com/DrUpauli.
3. Quoted in Leon J. Poddles, *Losing the Good Portion: Why Men are Alienated From Christianity* (South Bend, IN: St. Augustine's Press, 2018), 220.
4. "Muscular Christianity," Wikipedia

Chapter 1

1. Adam Sinicki, "Your Infinite Potential: Marvels of the Human Body," The Bioneer, January 5, 2021, https://www.thebioneer.com/infinite-human-potential/.
2. "What is the Smallest Blood Vessel in the Body?" Reference.com, March 4, 2020, https://www.reference.com/science/smallest-blood-vessel-body-46b97857ca2f9213.
3. "Diameter of a Human Hair," The Physics Factbook, accessed June 30 2023, https://hypertextbook.com/facts/1999/BrianLey.shtml.
4. "What is the Smallest Blood Vessel in the body?"
5. Norman Doidge, *The Brain that Changes Itself* (New York, NY: Ballantine Books, 2010), 53.
6. Siniki, "Your Infinite Potential."
7. Mary Bates, "Super Powers for the Blind and Deaf," Scientific American, September 18, 2012, https://www.scientificamerican.com/article/superpowers-for-the-blind-and-deaf/.

Also a YouTube video that demonstrates this phenomenon. It was uploaded by "chewbster": https://www.youtube.com/watch?v=GwGmWqX0MnM&ab_channel=chewbster.

8. T. R. Kral, et al., "Impact of short- and long-term mindfulness meditation training on amygdala reactivity to emotional stimuli," *NeuroImage*, 181, (2018): 301–313. https://doi.org/10.1016/j.neuroimage.2018.07.013.

9. D. Laneri, et al., "Mindfulness meditation regulates anterior insula activity during empathy for social pain," *Human Brain Mapping*, 38, no. 8, (2017): 4034–4046. https://doi.org/10.1002/hbm.23646.

10. Andrew Newberg, *How God Changes Your Brain: Breakthrough Findings from a Leading Neuroscientist*, (New York, NY: Ballantine Books, 2010) refers to the anterior cingulate as the "neurological heart" in chapter 1 as a part of the section "Learning to Feel Compassion."

11. Andrew Newberg Interview, *The Mind Health Report*, August 25, 2016, https://web.archive.org/web/20160825041338/http://fgbt.org:80/Health-Tips/strengthen-your-brain-through-the-power-of-prayer.html.

12. Barbara Fredrickson, *Love 2.0: Creating Happiness and Health in Moments of Connection* (New York, NY: Plume, 2013), 84.

13. "Is Christianity Harmful?" InspiringPhilosophy, accessed June 30, 2023, https://www.youtube.com/watch?v=FnbHal6vL4o.

14. E. Griesbauer, et al., "Learning the Knowledge: How London Taxi Drivers Build Their Cognitive Map of London," DOI

Foundation, 2021,
https://doi.org/10.1101/2021.06.04.447168.

15. Amy Cuddy, "Your Body Language May Shape Who You Are," TED Talk, October 1, 2012,
https://www.youtube.com/watch?v=Ks-_Mh1QhMc.

16. "Humans have not evolved to exercise, says Harvard prof," CBC, February 9, 2021, https://www.cbc.ca/radio/thecurrent/the-current-for-feb-9-2021-1.5906730/humans-have-not-evolved-to-exercise-says-harvard-prof-1.5907580.

17. Quoted in Poddles, *Losing the Good Portion*, 223.

18. J. Calatayud, et al., "Importance of Mind-Muscle Connection During Progressive Resistance Training," *European Journal of Applied Physiology*, 116, no. 3, (2015): 527–533, https://doi.org/10.1007/s00421-015-3305-7.

19. B. C. Clark, et al., "The Power of the Mind: The Cortex As a Critical Determinant of Muscle Strength/Weakness," Journal of Neurophysiology, 112, no. 12, (2014): 3219–3226. https://doi.org/10.1152/jn.00386.2014.

20. D. W. Kearns, and J. Crossman, "Effects of a Cognitive Intervention Package on the Free-Throw Performance of Varsity Basketball Players During Practice and Competition," *Perceptual and Motor Skills*, 75, no. 3 suppl., (1992): 1243–1253, https://doi.org/10.2466/pms.1992.75.3f.1243.

Chapter 2

1. Tertullian wrote in the collection, De Spectaculis, about this. Particularly in *Apology*, ch. 9.

2. Poddles, *Losing the Good Portion*, 91.

3. Poddles, *Losing the Good Portion*, 92.

4. Ibid.

5. C. S. Lewis, *Mere Christianity* (San Francisco, CA: HarperOne, 2017), 127.

6. John Eldridge, *Wild at Heart* (Nashville, TN: Thomas Nelson, 2021), 76.

Chapter 3

1. W. D. Edwards, et al. "On the Physical Death of Jesus Christ," *JAMA*, 255, no. 11, (1986): 1455, https://doi.org/10.1001/jama.1986.03370110077025. As for the weight of the cross: M. McKinley, "What's 'True' about the Cross That Killed Jesus?" CNN, April 2, 2015, https://www.cnn.com/2015/03/23/living/jesus-true-cross/index.html. As for the distance He had to travel: J. M. Jordan, "How Far Did Jesus Carry the Cross?" *Christian Faith Guide*, June 1, 2023, https://christianfaithguide.com/how-far-did-jesus-carry-the-cross/.

2. Poddles, *Losing the Good Portion*, 223.

Chapter 4

1. Lewis, *Mere Christianity*, 78.

2. "The Slowest Animals In The World," Safaris Africana, accessed June 30, 2023, https://safarisafricana.com/slowest-animals/.

3. Jocko Willink, "Discipline = Freedom," accessed June 30, 2023, https://www.youtube.com/watch?v=eBmVv2P-v2s.

Chapter 5

1. George Strait, "Good Time," on *Here for a Good Time*, MCA Nashville, 2011.
2. Big Sean, "Blessings," Ft. Drake, Kanye West, on *Dark Sky Paradise*, GOOD Music, 2015.
3. D. DeMarco, "Sartre: 'Atheism is a cruel, long-term business …'" The Interim, February 22, 2002, https://the-interim.com/columnist/donald-demarco/sartre-%E2%80%98atheism-is-a-cruel-long-term-business-%E2%80%A6/.
4. William Lane Craig, "The Absurdity of Life Without God," accessed June 30, 2023, https://www.youtube.com/watch?v=ZqNTT0E_T70.
5. Friedrich Nietzsche, *On the Genealogy of Morality* (Cambridge, United Kingdom: Cambridge University Press, 2006), 120.
6. Friedrich Nietzsche, *The Gay Science* (New York , NY: Vintage, 1974), 85.
7. Jason Hehir, *The Last Dance*, Netflix, 2020.
8. Theodore Roosevelt, *The Strenuous Life and Other Essays* (Mineola, NY: Dover Publications, 2009), 1. Although the original speech was delivered in Chicago, IL, USA, on April 10, 1899.
9. M. Elliott and M. J. Doane, "Religion, Psychological Well-Being, and Health," *Encyclopedia of Quality of Life and Well-Being Research,* (2014): 5469–5474. https://doi.org/10.1007/978-94-007-0753-5_4128.
10. Y. Chen, E. S. Kim, and T. J. VanderWeele, "Religious-service attendance and subsequent health and well-being

throughout adulthood: Evidence from three prospective cohorts." *International Journal of Epidemiology*, 49, no. 6, (2020): 2030–2040. https://doi.org/10.1093/ije/dyaa120.

11. Megan Brenan, "Americans' Mental Health Ratings Sink to New Low," Gallup, December 7, 2020, https://news.gallup.com/poll/327311/americans-mental-health-ratings-sink-new-low.aspx.

12. W. B. Wilcox, J. S. Carroll, and L. Derose, "Religious men can be devoted dads, too," *The New York Times*, May 18, 2019, https://www.nytimes.com/2019/05/18/opinion/sunday/happy-marriages.html.

Chapter 6

1. "Leading Causes of Death," CDC, accessed June 30, 2023, https://www.cdc.gov/nchs/fastats/leading-causes-of-death.htm.

2. "Injuries Higher Among Obese People, Study Finds," ScienceDaily, July 21, 2005, https://www.sciencedaily.com/releases/2005/07/050721061850.htm.

3. "Exercise and stress: Get moving to manage stress," Mayo Clinic, accessed June 30, 2023, https://www.mayoclinic.org/healthy-lifestyle/stress-management/in-depth/exercise-and-stress/art-20044469.

4. Claire McCarthy, "Anxiety in Teens is Rising: What's going on?" HealthyChildren.org, November 20,2019, https://www.healthychildren.org/English/health-issues/conditions/emotional-problems/Pages/Anxiety-Disorders.aspx.

5. John Ratey, "Can exercise help treat anxiety?" Harvard Health Publishing, October 24, 2019,

https://www.health.harvard.edu/blog/can-exercise-help-treat-anxiety-2019102418096.

6. John Ratey, *Spark: The Revolutionary New Science of Exercise and the Brain* (New York, NY: Little Brown Spark, 2013), Chapter 7: Addiction.

Chapter 7

1. Matt Walsh, *Church of Cowards: A Wake-Up Call to Complacent Christians* (Washington, DC: Regenery Gateway, 2020). 30-31

2. M. Elliott and M. J. Doane, "Religion, Psychological Well-Being, and Health," *Encyclopedia of Quality of Life and Well-Being Research*, 2014, 5469–5474, https://doi.org/10.1007/978-94-007-0753-5_4128.

3. Kimberley Richards, "Damian Lillard Garners Praise For Old Quote On Real Pressures For Everyday People," HuffPost, April 30, 2019, https://www.huffpost.com/entry/damian-lillard-pressure-quote-blaz-ers_n_5cc87047e4b05379114bb6eb.

4. John F. Trepanowski and Richard J. Bloomer, "The impact of religious fasting on human health," *Nutrition Journal*, 9, no. 57, 2010, https://doi.org/10.1186/1475-2891-9-57. And: Olsen, N. (2020). "What happens if you don't eat for a day?" *Medical News Today*. January 5, 2020, https://www.medicalnewstoday.com/articles/322065#other-effects.

   As for increasing testosterone: "How fasting changes testosterone (fasting science)," What I've Learned, accessed February 18, 2023, https://www.youtube.com/watch?v=k1OMGDnGpIk.

Chapter 8

1. Youri Oh, "Fashion in politics: what makes Korean female politicians wear 'the suit' not 'a dress'?" *International Journal of Fashion Design, Technology and Education*, 12, no. 3, (2019): 374–384, https://doi.org/10.1080/17543266.2019.1616832.

2. Sandra Praxmarer, "How a presenter's perceived attractiveness affects persuasion for attractiveness-unrelated products," *International Journal of Advertising*, 30, no. 5, (2011): 839–865, https://doi.org/10.2501/ija-30-5-839-865.

3. Justin J. Gunnell and Stephen J. Ceci, "When emotionality trumps reason: A study of individual processing style and juror bias," *Behavioral Sciences & the Law*, 28, no. 6, (2010): 850–877, https://doi.org/10.1002/bsl.939.

4. Paul Uponi, "What is the Point of Living?" https://allmylinks.com/what-is-the-point-of-living.

5. Brett and Kate McKay, *Muscular Christianity: The Relationship Between Men and Faith* (Jenks, OK: Semper Virilis Publishing, 2018). 50

Chapter 9

1. BDNF is explained in the glossary and second chapter (Learning) of John J. Ratey's *Spark: The Revolutionary New Science of Exercise and the Brain*, (New York, NY: Little Brown Spark, 2013).

2. J. B. Grissom, "Physical fitness and academic achievement," *Journal of Exercise Physiology Online*, 8, no. 1, (2005): 11–25,

https://www.researchgate.net/publication/235914141_Physical_fitness_and_academic_achievement.

3. Frances O'Callaghan, et al., "Physical Activity and Intelligence: A Causal Exploration," *Journal of Physical Activity and Health*, 9, no. 2, (2012): 218–224. https://doi.org/10.1123/jpah.9.2.218.

4. William Butler, *Charles George Gordon* (Charleston, SC: BiblioBazaar, 2009), 85.

5. Karl Smallwood, "Leonardo da Vinci Could Kick Your Ass," FactFiend, accessed June 30, 2023, http://www.factfiend.com/leonardo-da-vinci-could-kick-your-ass/.

6. Joyce Gomes-Osman, et al., "Exercise for cognitive brain health in aging: A systematic review for an evaluation of dose," *Neurology, Clinical Practice*, 8, no. 3, (2018): 257–265, https://doi.org/10.1212/CPJ.0000000000000460.

7. "Sport at the New Frontier: The Soft American," *Sports Illustrated*, 13, no. 26, (December 26, 1960), 14–17.

Chapter 10

1. Brenton M. Asken, et al., "Research Gaps and Controversies in Chronic Traumatic Encephalopathy: A Review," *JAMA Neurology*, 74, no. 10, (2017): 1255–1262, https://doi.org/10.1001/jamaneurol.2017.2396.

2. "Sexual claim transformed perception of Wilt." Associated Press, October 13, 1999 (retrieved March 29, 2022, via ESPN).

3. "Powerful priest pulls a fire truck with his heavenly muscles," *New York Post*, accessed June 30, 2023,

https://www.youtube.com/watch?v=fK5PAiESyiI&ab_chan
nel=NewYorkPost.

4. Chad Bonham, *Serving: True Champions Know That Success Takes Sacrifice.* (Ventura, CA: Gospel Light, 2008), 69.

5. Beth Reese Cravey, "Tim Tebow Takes Time to Meet Families in Crisis Amid Hoopla of Playoffs," *The Florida Times-Union*, January 11, 2012.

6. Bob Tedeschi, "A Chaste Tim Tebow Will Have Company in New York," *The New York Times*, August 21, 2012.

7. Jemele Hill, "Tebow practices what he preaches," ESPN, July 27, 2009, http://www.espn.com/espn/page2/story?sportCat=ncf&page=hill/090724.

8. Nancy R. Pearcey, *The Toxic War on Masculinity: How Christianity Reconciles the Sexes*, (Ada. MI: Baker Books, 2023). 183

Chapter 11

1. Jack Donovan, *The Way of Men*, (Milwaukie. OR: Dissonant Hum, 2012). 47

2. Steven Johnson, *Everything Bad Is Good For You: How Today's Popular Culture Is Actually Making Us Smarter* (New York, NY: Riverhead Books, 2006), 28.

Chapter 12

1. Theodore Roosevelt, quoted in "Semper Virilis: A Roadmap to Manhood in the 21st Century," The Art of Manliness, June 9, 2014, https://www.artofmanliness.com/character/behavior/semper-virilis-a-roadmap-to-manhood-in-the-21st-century/.

2. Thomas Carter, *Coach Carter*, MTV Films, 2005.

3. Epictetus, *The Art of Living: The Classical Manual on Virtue, Happiness and Effectiveness* (San Francisco, CA: HarperOne, 2017), 79.

Chapter 13

1. R. Koestner, C. Franz, and J. Weinberger, "The family origins of empathic concern: A 26-year longitudinal study," *Journal of Personality and Social Psychology*, 58, no. 4, (1990): 709–717, https://doi.org/10.1037/0022-3514.58.4.709.

2. M. Ann Easterbrooks and Wendy A. Goldberg, "Toddler Development in the Family: Impact of Father Involvement and Parenting Characteristics," *JSTOR*, 55, no. 3, (1984): 740. https://doi.org/10.2307/1130126.

3. Anthony T. DeBenedet and Lawrence J. Cohen, *The Art of Roughhousing: Good Old-Fashioned Horseplay and Why Every Kid Needs It* (Philadelphia, PA: Quirk Books, 2011), 21.

4. Ralph F. Wilson, "The Command and Blessing of Holy Sex," Jesus Walk, accessed June 30, 2023, https://www.jesus-walk.com/thessalonians/04_sex.htm.

5. Thomas Aquinas, *Summa Theologica*, 2-2, Q.158.

6. Michael Dante DiMartino and Bryan Konietzko, *Avatar: The last Airbender*, Nickelodeon Animation Studios with Studio Mir, 2005–2008.

7. Aristotle, *Nicomachean Ethics*, 4.1–5.

8. Friedrich Nietzsche, *Beyond Good and Evil* (Cambridge, United Kingdom: Cambridge University Press, 2001), 44.

9. Walter Wink, "Jesus' Third Way: Nonviolent Engagement." In *Engaging the Powers: Discernment and Resistance in a World of Domination* (Minneapolis, MN: Augsburg Fortress, 1992), 175–195.

10. *Merriam-Webster*, s.v. "murder," accessed June 30, 2023, https://www.merriam-webster.com/dictionary/murder.

11. Paul Gondreau, *The Passions of Christ's Soul in the Theology of St. Thomas Aquinas* (Providence, RI: Cluny Media, LLC, 2018), 37.

12. *Avatar: The Last Airbender.*

13. Makoto Yukimura, *Vinland Saga*, Kodansha, 2005.

14. Alexander Moseley, "Just War Theory," Internet Encyclopedia of Philosophy, accessed June 30, 2023, https://iep.utm.edu/justwar/.

15. Masashi Kishimoto, *Naruto*, Shueisha, 1999–2014.

Chapter 14

1. "Women more likely than men to affiliate with a religion," Pew Research Center, March 22, 2016, https://www.pewresearch.org/religion/2016/03/22/women-more-likely-than-men-to-affiliate-with-a-religion/.

2. Julia DeCelles-Zwerneman, "Where Are All the Men? Exploring the Gender Gap in Church," Capterra, August 10, 2016, https://www.capterra.com/resources/where-are-all-the-men-exploring-the-gender-gap-in-church/.

3. Werner Haug, et al., eds., "The Demographic Characteristics of Linguistic and Religious Groups in Switzerland." In *The Demographic Characteristics of National Minorities in Certain European States, Population Studies*, No. 31, Vol. 2,

(Strasbourg, France: Council of Europe Publishing, 2000), 154.

4. Elizabeth Cady Stanton, one of the godmothers of feminism, reportedly said that "the Bible and the church have been the greatest stumbling blocks in the way of women's emancipation."

5. Leon J. Poddles, *The Church Impotent: The Feminization of Christianity* (Dallas, TX: Spence Publishing Company, 1999), 19.

6. *Vinland Saga.*

7. Summaries of YouTube videos by Adam Lane Smith, "Men bond better through vasopressin than oxytocin. Here's how to make that happen," accessed November 12, 2021, https://www.youtube.com/watch?v=1Llz-GR-HWY; and "How to make him bond to you by increasing vasopressin," accessed June 8, 2022, https://www.youtube.com/watch?v=fKDO1PPwCH4; along with my own personal messages sent to Smith.

8. While not formally an IQ test, military members do take an aptitude test. If they score the equivalent of an IQ of 80, they will not be admitted. For a more detailed answer, see https://law.stackexchange.com/questions/37491/is-it-truly-illegal-for-the-us-armed-forces-to-hire-someone-whose-iq-is-less-tha/37493#37493.

9. Robert P. Burriss, Hannah M. Rowland, and Anthony C. Little, "Facial scarring enhances men's attractiveness for short-term relationships," Science Direct, *Elsevier*, 46, no. 2 (2009): 213–217. https://doi.org/10.1016/j.paid.2008.09.029

10. Eldridge, *Wild at Heart*, 9.

11. "American Religious Identification Survey," Graduate Center, City University of New York, 2001.
12. Jonathan A. Lanman and Michael D. Buhrmester, "Religious actions speak louder than words: exposure to credibility-enhancing displays predicts theism," *Religion, Brain & Behavior*, 7, no. 1, (2016): 3–16, https://doi.org/10.1080/2153599x.2015.1117011.
13. John Gray, *Men Are From Mars, Women Are From Venus* (San Francisco, CA: HarperCollins, 2012), 12.
14. Ibid., passim.
15. I used a mix of different sources to come up with a full definition of *thumos*. The part about *thumos* being a spring of righteous rage is implied from Puddles, *Losing the Good Portion*, p. 26. The part about it being associated with energy, blood, recognition, and a rebellion against evil is implied on pages 25 and 221.
16. David Murrow, *Why Men Hate Going to Church*, (Nashville, TN: Thomas Nelson, 2011) 34.
17. Ibid., 65.
18. Eiichiro Oda, *One Piece* manga (Tokyo, Japan: Shueisha, 2010).
19. 19 Oda, *One Piece*, ch. 576.
20. Poddles, *Losing the Good Portion*, 225.
21. Murrow, *Why Men Hate Going to Church*, 51.
22. Oda, *One Piece*, ch. 485.
23. Murrow, *Why Men Hate Going to Church*, 166.
24. Illustration adapted from Murrow, *Why Men Hate Going to Church*, 164.

Chapter 15

1. Christopher Kaczor, *The Gospel of Happiness: How Secular Psychology Points to the Wisdom of Christian Practice* (South Bend, IN: St Augustine Press, 2019), 108.

2. Sebastiao Barbosa-Netto, et al. (2021). "Self-Selected Resistance Exercise Load: Implications for Research and Prescription," *Journal of Strength and Conditioning Research*, 35, no. 1, https://doi.org/10.1519/jsc.0000000000002287.

3. Adam Sinicki, "Functional Aesthetics: Bodybuilding X Functional Training," The Bioneer, July 22, 2021, https://www.thebioneer.com/functional-aesthetics/.

4. Steve Kotler, *Art of the Impossible: A Peak Performance Primer* (San Francisco: HarperOne, 2021), 70-71.

5. Brad J. Schoenfeld, et al., "Resistance training volume enhances muscle hypertrophy but not strength in trained men," *Medicine & Science in Sports & Exercise*, 51, no. 1, (2019): 94–103, https://doi.org/10.1249/mss.0000000000001764.

Printed in the USA
CPSIA information can be obtained
at www.ICGtesting.com
LVHW091246271123
764762LV00059B/2027

9 781739 055509